# THE HEAVY HORSE MANUAL

# THE
# HEAVY HORSE
# MANUAL

Nick Rayner and Keith Chivers

*Photographs by Barry Rickman* AMPA

DAVID & CHARLES
Newton Abbot London North Pomfret (Vt)

(*previous page*) Nick Rayner driving his three-horse team pulling a disc harrow

**British Library Cataloguing in Publication Data**

Rayner, Nick
  The heavy horse manual.
  1. Draft horses
  I. Title    II. Chivers, Keith
  636.1'5'0941    SF11

ISBN 0-7153-8057-5

Library of Congress Catalog Card Number: 80-85501

© Nick Rayner and Keith Chivers 1981

Typeset, printed and bound in Great Britain
by Butler & Tanner Limited, Frome and London
for David & Charles (Publishers) Limited
Brunel House Newton Abbot Devon

Published in the United States of America
by David & Charles Inc
North Pomfret Vermont 05053 USA

# Contents

Acknowledgments                                    8

1   Making Your Mind Up                            9

2   Spending Your Money Wisely                    27

3   Basic Creature Comforts                       49

4   Healthy Mind and Healthy Body                 64

5   Work on the Farm                              85

6   Harness                                       99

7   Breaking and Training                        131

8   Your Horse on Parade                         147

9   Breeding and Young Life                      176

    Postscript                                   199

    Further Reading and Information              202

    Index                                        203

# List of Illustrations

Clydesdales and Shires harrowing at a 'working'    10
Percherons delivering beer at Southwold    14-15
Suffolks should really be photographed in colour    19
A stall showing manger, hay-rack and salt-lick    41
This loose box is 14ft by 12ft    43
Grooming kit, laid out on a stable rubber    58
Using an electric groomer    61
Not many beginners are going to acquire a horse with a
   perfect foot    79
Side-raking hay with a Bamford's FGN side-rake    87
A dung-cart is essentially a fixed-side tipping vehicle    88
The scotch cart is the most useful general-purpose farm
   cart    89
A slurry cart explains itself, but it can also be used as a
   water-cart    90
A wide variety of trailed implements can be towed behind
   a hitch cart    91
Chain-harrowing, using a hitch cart    93
Rolling a seed-bed with a pair of horses and a tractor-
   roller    94-5
A modern British-made horse-drawn dung-spreader    96
Three machines now imported from Poland    97
To prevent injury, any halter must be knotted like this    101
The size of a collar is determined by the inside measure-
   ment    102
Too big a collar will 'wring' a horse's shoulders    103
A collar that is too tight will choke him    104
This collar is just right    105
A collection of bits    108
This is the safe way to shorten your lines    110
A dangerous way to shorten your lines    111
This horse is hitched all wrong    113

Here we have a vast improvement on the effort shown in
    the previous picture     113
A trace-harness spreader     119
Hooking up the slack in traces     121
This is basic plough-harness     122
The tie-backs are well shown in this picture     124-5
A pair of Thwaites' black Shire geldings     126
A farm gelding in show harness     128
These two horses are wearing full Cornish decorated
    harness     129
How not to get into a cart     132
The correct way to get into a cart     133
Breaking harness, with a mouthing bit     134
A young horse's first load should be a log, or something
    similar     137
This horse is learning to back into shafts     139
Teaching a horse to meet all eventualities on the road     143
Gentle persuasion in loading up     144
He is now used to being loaded up     145
Start plaiting as close behind the ears as possible     148
The flights should be plaited in with the bass     148
For a horse to be shown in harness, carry on plaiting to
    just in front of his collar     148
Start plaiting as high up the tail as you can     150
Tie on your tail-loop and cover with ribbon     150
Warm water, a good animal shampoo and a water brush
    will get a leg clean     155
Stand the horse's foot on a split-open sack     155
Mr W. C. Saunders' team of Suffolks     163
A modest agricultural turn-out     164-5
Colonel and Punch, two of Nick Rayner's horses     169
A Percheron and a Shire drilling corn at a spring 'working'     171
Nick Rayner's Broadley Colonel     173

# Acknowledgments

We are enormously indebted to Barry Rickman AMPA of Brockenhurst in Hampshire whose forty-one photographs, specially taken for this book, comprise the bulk of the illustrations.

Our thanks are due also to the following for permission to use the other photographs taken or owned by them and credited in the captions: Anne Ford-Lloyd FRPS, J. A. Adnams of Adnams and Company Ltd, Southwold, Sheilagh Andrews, Colin and Janet Fry, David Kay of Daniel Thwaites and Co Ltd, Blackburn, Edward Clapham, Gordon Adlam, the Suffolk Horse Society, and Lee Weatherley.

We appreciate the tolerance shown by Maureen Rayner and Joan Chivers towards husbands who talked for hours on end, filled rooms with smoke and ate and drank at frequent intervals. And we thank Susan Rumney for typing the manuscript.

# 1

# Making Your Mind Up

If all be true that I do think,
There are five reasons we should drink:
Good wine - a friend - or being dry -
Or lest we should be, by and by -
Or any other reason why.

In the old days, people had only one reason for wanting a heavy horse - there was something to be pulled, and lorries and tractors had not yet been invented. When, after the Second World War, the diesel engine drove cart-horses off the land and the remaining few off the town streets, there seemed no reason at all. Nowadays, there appear to be as many as there are for drinking, if not more. In discussing the validity of some of these, it will be simplest to divide potential owners of heavy horses into three groups: farmers; commercial or industrial firms; and amateurs. But in fact, many who seem to belong to either of the first two categories are really to be classified with the third.

Henry Aldrich, whose well-known verse comprehensively vindicated the drinker, mentioned only one sort of drink. The cart-horse is one sort of horse but, like wine, is of many varieties - permutations of colour, breed, age, sex and, of course, origin or pedigree.

## The farmer

The virtues of the horse do not rival the immense power, tirelessness and speed of the tractor, but are complementary to them. On 2000 arable acres there is not really a place for him, but there certainly is on a mixed farm.

Firstly, he is immeasurably cheaper, except where the sheer quickness of the tractor is overwhelmingly advantageous or its power essential. It will be impossible for you to work out the figures in the way a town-user can do, even if you are fond of sophisticated costings. You are more likely to regard horse-keep as being lost to sight among other expenses - and you will not be far wrong. If you can also breed

9

A mixed four-horse team harrowing at a 'working'. On the off side a pair of Clydesdales, a pair of Shires on the near side. Clydesdales generally, as here, have more white up the leg (*Anne Ford-Lloyd FRPS*)

a few extra ones, you will show a profit. There is money in what people want, especially when supply cannot meet the demand.

Secondly, the horse has intelligence and a remarkable memory, and can be moved about by remote control through the voice. Its brain, like its strength, lies half way between that of man and tractor. This asset sometimes actually saves labour, one man being able to do what, with an inanimate machine, would require two.

Thirdly, the horse can go into awkward places where the tractor cannot. He can also tread on wet or heavy ground which the tractor would tear to pieces or flatten into a solid lump.

Fourthly, horses are ecologically admirable, consuming only new vegetable matter instead of fossil fuel; not polluting the environment; not impoverishing the soil but making a little contribution to its enrichment by their dung and urine.

We have said nothing about fuel shortages. But who knows what might happen? In ten or twenty years, everyone might be rushing to get horses. If all the mixed or stock farmers in the land suddenly found that a quarter of their power could best be supplied by horses, a lot of money would be made by anyone who had established himself in the horse-breeding business.

In putting forward these points in favour of horses, we intend only to justify and encourage those who would like to keep just one or two. If you are such a person, you may find that your plan will initially lack support from your family or your staff. It is important to win their tolerance, if not their co-operation. The only people whose opinion you can entirely ignore are your neighbours and friends. One unfortunate element in the revival of interest in heavy horses is that the 'olde-tyme farming' theme is too often played. Some owners are even misguided enough to appear in the local show ring with a bit of twine round their legs, a muffler at their necks and a straw between their teeth. This gives the Great British Public a twitch in its camera finger, but anything which smacks of the sweat and toil and poverty of pre-war days is bad for the image of the modern working horse. How can a man who has to make a living from his farm be expected to take horses seriously if this is how they are presented? You have the brains to think out the economics of it, but your neighbours may make witty remarks. Take no notice. The more intelligent ones will either regard you as trendy or will see sense in what you are doing.

On the question of manpower, there is much unnecessary anxiety. If you employ staff, you are likely to have among them a really good chap who is loyal, hard-working and enthusiastic – a treasure in every respect except, perhaps, that he is not the most brilliant example of modern technological man. He does not hold a fistful of college qualifications. He would not want to fiddle with a tractor that had gone wrong: and if he did, he is the sort who would make it worse. As a worker and ally, however, he cannot be beaten. Or else there is such a man as this whom you could and would get, if only he could be fitted into your sophisticated scheme of operations. He certainly need not be an aged relic of the old horse era. There are plenty of young men who like horses.

If you allow such a chap to be the one who (among other things, of course) does the horse jobs, you will be amazed at the result. You may even find him thinking up extra things to do, and you will have to assess whether they are economic or only a waste of time and money. Of course, if you are very much a working farmer yourself, you may not like the idea. If this employee has charge of the horses, how will you get a turn yourself?

The problem of week-ends, of course, frightens many people off. But if you have stock, there must be someone about at times. It will not take long for whoever is on duty to feed and water the horses before he goes home, and many would welcome this particular chore.

The horse's actual work is a topic we consider in Chapter 5. If you want free replacements or some extra ones for sale at 90 per cent profit, Chapter 9, even though intended for the amateur, might be of help. But the fact that you are a farmer does not disqualify you from keeping a horse or two purely as a hobby – and you can indulge yourself at far less expense than the non-farmer. You might be a 2000-acre arable man, eager to have something on the place which moves of its own accord. Even so, your instinct will be to make such an interest pay. You could get some fun from buying foals or yearlings and enjoy watching them grow into money.

## Industry and commerce

The number of industrial and trading companies which own heavy horses is increasing. There are two reasons: (a) economy and (b) publicity. Some of the most famous horse-owning firms have in their stables animals which are kept purely for shows. However, the working horses also stamp their owners' names more indelibly upon the public mind than any other form of advertising can possibly do, by simply appearing in the streets, so let us start with these.

The mere idea may sound preposterous in view of conditions in our city streets. 'It is all right for the brewers' (we can almost hear you saying this) 'but not for me.' Yet the brewers, and they are not the only ones of course, have no divine rights or privileges in this matter. If they can operate successfully, why not you?

As an example, let us take a brewery which was among the first to dispense with horses and the first in modern times to reinstate them. Daniel Thwaites and Company of Blackburn gave up horses in 1927. A third of a century later, in 1960, they bought and started to use two work-horses. These were followed by one, then a pair, of show-horses and in 1964 by a team of four. These latter, which for years now have consistently stood at or near the top of the national 'first division', are not our present concern, but the work-horses are.

Messrs Thwaites' last precise comparative costing of horse and motor haulage on short journeys was made in 1978. The results were so much in favour of the horse that it has been superfluous to make another, because the difference has obviously increased rather than diminished. It would be misleading to quote actual sums of money, and so we shall have to counter inflation by using percentages.

In 1978, the cost of putting a four-year-old horse and dray on the road was 58.3 per cent of the cost of buying a motor lorry to carry the same weight ($2\frac{1}{2}$ tons). Calculations were based on the purchase of second-hand drays in good condition, rather than new ones. The reason was that the former could be bought without much difficulty, whereas it was not easy to find a body builder accustomed to the type of work required by brewers. However, demand produces supply, and more and more expert craftsmen are turning their attention to horse-drawn vehicles of all types. The future should be rosier, not darker.

A four-year-old horse was expected to work for fourteen years. It might not, of course. For the sake of simplicity, let us assume the dray would wear out at the same time. It actually would not, but since even a second-hand vehicle and harness costs two and a half times as much as a horse, the bonus in hand at the end of fourteen years if depreciation of the whole turn-out were calculated over that period of time would be sufficient to cater for the net cost (purchase less insurance or sale value) of having to replace the horse earlier than anticipated.

Motor vehicles, on the other hand, are usually written off over a seven-year period. It was assumed that the cost of a replacement in 1985 would have doubled compared with 1978. (This would have been so if inflation over the whole period were equivalent to a steady rate of between 10 and 11 per cent per annum.) In that case, the capital required over fourteen years for a horse and dray was slightly less than 19.5 per cent of that required for a motor lorry.

So far as annual or daily expenditure is concerned, it was found that insurance of horse and dray cost only slightly less than that of a motor vehicle, and could therefore be discounted. The wages bill was also more or less the same and this, too, could be left out of the reckoning. (Someone has to be paid to come back at night and feed the horses. Someone also has to be paid to grease motor waggons at night.)

However, this is only half the story, and the rest will probably be found to redress the balance. Most new operators would wish to make an economic comparison between a two-horse dray and a motor lorry to carry four tons. If this is done, it is likely that overheads and, in particular, horse-feed will cause the two addition sums – comprising wildly different individual figures – to result in almost identical totals.

Circumstances will vary enormously from one company to another. So will costs, and the only claim we would make is that the horse, for short-haulage, is no more expensive than the motor. It is for their boldness in flying in the face of fashion during the Sixties, and after prudently counting the cost as it applied to them, that Messrs Thwaites are to be congratulated.

13

A pair of Percherons delivering beer at Southwold, followed by a single. Percherons are either black or grey, the latter colour tending to become lighter with age (*J. A. Adnams*)

The re-introduction of genuine horse-power to Thwaites' in 1960 was due to David Kay, then aged 25. By tenacity and reasoned argument that heavy horses would be an economy, he had overcome almost total opposition by the hierarchy of his firm. He had joined the company as a stock-taker at the age of 17, and by 1960 had risen to the position of manager of the soft-drinks section. In 1964 he was general sales manager, and in 1980 became director and general manager. Such a company does not promote to its highest office a man with ideas which do not work. Nor does the Shire Horse Society elect as its youngest-ever President a man who has no weightier qualifications than a personal passion for horses.

Anyone considering the possibility of horses for industrial or trade work will obviously employ an expert foreman. This should be easier than twenty or thirty years ago, when candidates were becoming fewer and, through advancing years, less capable.

The top-class commercial horse-owners of today employ and train a growing number of intelligent and youthful men, highly skilled and articulate – a new breed of horsemen, well adapted to the contemporary scene. Though such firms will not thank you for poaching from their ranks, they will accept the fact that a competent man possibly cannot get to the top of his particular tree unless he is prepared to throw in his lot with one of the new employers in the town-horse business. He, in his turn, will find young chaps of similar mind to himself who are keen to learn how to drive a heavy horse – a job which nowadays is highly regarded.

Your horse venture will not thrive unless you, as the boss, take an intelligent and personal interest. However complex the structure of your company, and however remote you may be from your employees, lack of communication and personal relationship will never do when there are horses about. The foreman, if he is worth his salt, will expect to deal with you personally, not with some middle manager. It is you who must wander from time to time into his stable, and you must address him by his first name. In some ways he is more important than you, for he can do the image of your company more good (or more harm) than anyone else in the firm. And the same applies to the drivers who work under him, and their horses.

A detailed study of heavy horses at work in industry has recently been commissioned by the Shire Horse Society, and is likely to be reported around publication of this book.

\*     \*     \*

Horses for showing are an entirely different proposition from work-horses. The point to remember is that nowadays this sort of publicity is *good* publicity. Thirty years ago, only the Queen, the Lord Mayor of London and the brewers, all of whom had something to gain by an image that reminded us of tradition and the good old days, were exempt from the finger of scorn at being associated in any way with the horse-and-cart era. But that situation has totally changed. The public, accustomed to far more outlandish and irrelevant forms of publicity-seeking sponsorship than this, regard the smart turn-out as a token of a company's standing, stability and good customer-relations.

Common sense will tell you how far to go. There is not much point in exhibiting at the Royal Show if you happen to be a builder's merchant whose farthest-flung customer is only twenty miles from your office in Barchester or Casterbridge. Sufficient that people will fall over themselves to get you to local shows and fêtes where your name means something and could mean more.

The obvious thing to do is to pay a professional horseman to do everything for you. He will keep the one or two horses and the waggon at his premises and arrange to show them, while you and members of your staff enjoy a day out whenever you can. At the bigger shows, do not expect your name to head the class immediately. It may take a little while to get your name and your horses known, but your turn will come.

On second thoughts, and if your aims are modest and very local, are you really going to hand over everything and pay someone else to enjoy himself? If you have a few acres, you might decide to have a go yourself. To relax from the stress and strain of modern business, you might find a horse more therapeutic than golf, sailing, fishing or scotch.

### The amateur

There are today countless ponies, dogs and other creatures who suffer, either from neglect (usually casual rather than chronic) or from witless over-kindness that provides them with all the things unnecessary for, and indeed harmful to, their well-being. God forbid that cart-horses should be added to the list.

It does not matter a fig what your motive is for keeping a heavy horse. 'Any other reason why' is defensible, provided you can keep him fit and happy. He cannot be happy unless he is fit, or fit unless he is happy, or happy and fit unless he is reasonably occupied in body and mind. The purpose of this book is as much to help you decide whether you can manage this as to advise on how you can do it.

Some people fancy the idea of showing their horse, or having a go at ploughing matches. Others wish to play at being a farmer on two or three acres, or to try their hand at breeding a foal or two. In most cases, the underlying purpose is to enjoy the good life on Saturdays and Sundays, even if the rat-race claims them from Monday until Friday.

Certain men, although they would not admit it, seem to think of a heavy horse as the latest status symbol, or are secretly jealous of their daughters, who have ponies. We have our doubts about these chaps. One man was looking for a cart-horse because, he frankly but enigmatically avowed, it would be 'a challenge'. A challenge to see how long he could keep it alive? An odd motive, but it might turn out all right. Another had acquired a horse-drawn caravan and bought a horse to pull him away on holiday. But he loaded the van with so much heavy gear that, after ten miles, his undersized slave, which had previously done no work for a year, could hardly stand up.

There are also kindly souls who think it would be a splendid gesture to give a couple of old horses a good home in which to pass their last days. And Granny, too, would love to go and pat them on Sunday afternoons, if it is fine. They should think again. Nothing in this book is for them, except the Postscript.

But the rest of you, read on. If anything that follows puts you off the idea, we are sorry for you, but perhaps glad for the horse you might have bought. True love sometimes means renunciation and self-sacrifice. To those amateurs who are not deflected, we wish good luck.


### What sort of horse?

If there are seven ages of man, there are six of a cart-horse – and five basic colours (with roan variations), four breeds, three sexes and two classes (pedigree and non-pedigree). Let us try to sort these out.

*Sex and age*
Clearly, you are not going to buy a stallion: it is a choice between a mare and a gelding. If you are determined to jump in at the deep end by breeding, then of course it will be a mare. But if you are patient enough to wade in gradually, then start with a gelding.

Suffolks, more than any other breed, should really be photographed in colour, so that we may enjoy their chestnut glory. These live in Wiltshire and belong to Mrs Sheilagh Andrews (*Sheilagh Andrews*)

A gelding and a mare are of equal merit for both work and showing. The mare might be somewhat temperamental and touchy when she is on heat. A gelding is even-tempered, week in and week out. On the other hand, if something goes wrong with a gelding, he can only become meat. A similar accident or misfortune suffered by a mare might not prevent her breeding. However, for your first horse, this is a minor consideration. You might as well leave the mares for those who wish to breed from them.

You may have it at the back of your mind to breed in a few years' time, or when you feel confident enough to do so. In that case, still begin with a gelding. A mare that has become middle-aged without being got in foal may not be able to breed at all, especially if under-experience or over-ambition in the show ring has led you into keeping her too fat and too inactive for too long.

However, at the risk of appearing self-contradictory, we should add that if you start by looking for a gelding, there is nothing strongly against acquiring a mare instead. It might be possible to buy one very reasonably simply because someone else has tried to breed from her and failed, and at the age of six or seven she is now less likely than ever to produce a first foal. So her owner is prepared to sell her to you. For 'gelding' therefore, you can read 'non-breeding mare'.

Your first horse ought to be a fully grown animal. Let someone else take the risk of seeing him through the stage of infantile ailments. And let someone else get him broken and trained for work or the show ring. You want an animal that can teach you, not an unruly pupil. A young inexperienced horse and an inexperienced owner are together sure to court disaster. Five years is a good minimum age. The horse is in his early prime and ought to be a decent gelding that anyone can work and handle. Should you want to exchange him for something else in two or three years' time, his value would have diminished scarcely at all.

If you must buy a mare for breeding, try to go for one that has already had a foal. That will give you some assurance that she is capable of having another. You might be able to get one that has had a foal at four. She will be six by the time she can produce one for you, unless she is already in-foal again when you buy her. The price will be high if her first offspring was any good. If it is too high, a maiden three- or four-year-old would be better than a brood mare which you suspect may be nearing the end of her career. And an elderly one that no one has ever bred from is the worst proposition of all. Even if she has a foal, she might 'starve' it, or feed it and 'starve' herself.

There is one other consideration when buying a brood mare. If she is also to take part in a programme of work, ask yourself if her services can be partly or wholly dispensed with for an indefinite period perhaps before and certainly after foaling. She will do a lot for you during the year, but she cannot be a full-time worker all the time.

*Class*
Let us start at the top, and work down the social scale.

*Pedigreed animals* You would buy a pure-bred mare only if you wanted a potential prize-winner fully qualified to appear even at the top shows, or if you would like her offspring, male as well as female, to be automatically eligible for the stud-book. You would be like the learner-motorist who begins his lessons in a Rolls-Royce.

A gelding of course does not possess a pedigree certificate – unless, when very young, he was considered a potential stallion and was submitted for registration in the appropriate stud-book. In that case, he might come to you with a full pedigree, but this is of the same practical value as an out-of-date passport, because it is of no value even as a qualification for shows, as we shall see.

If you expect your new animal to be a good worker as well as a beauty and an aristocrat, you might possibly be disappointed. Blue-blooded show-horses may never have done any real work. They are sometimes more scatter-brained than others and less willing and sensible where honest toil is required. But to overstate this point would be a greater distortion of the truth than not to mention it at all. We shall just say that the great champion is sometimes the dumb blonde of the horse world.

Furthermore, in modern times there is a danger that the criteria used by show judges might be dictated less by the consideration whether the animals before them are so constructed that they are likely to work efficiently for long hours and for many years than by an abstract ideal based upon the points laid down (originally for good practical reasons) by the breed society and, inevitably, upon their own personal prejudices as to what constitutes the perfect animal. For example, in the hard old days, the Shire was rightly supposed to be a tall animal on short legs: now it is not on short legs.

*The grade animal* Below full-pedigree status, one might buy a mare whose sire is registered in the stud-book of its breed, but whose dam is not. She might actually have a certificate of some sort from the appropriate breed society, which may operate a 'grade register' for this type. Her dam, in practice, will be lacking rather in identity papers than in blood, for an inspection is necessary before the daughter can go into this register.

Filly foals produced by such a mare would be eligible for a higher grade if got by a registered stallion. In three or four generations, according to your particular society's rules, you could get to the position where your latest filly foal qualifies for the stud-book proper.

The idea of grading-up might appeal to you, and is certainly fun.

You might even start with a modestly priced animal and end up with a real winner. But your colt foals, all down the line until you have one from a fully registered mare, will be due for castration, however good they are, because there is no 'grading' for them. In addition, even the most careful study of form and of the stud-books might be completely upset by hereditary factors which no one could take into account, simply through lack of information about one half of your first mare's ancestry.

In the case of geldings, ancestry in the female line is of no importance, provided that the individual animal is a good one, since, even at the top shows, the only requirement is that they must be by a registered sire. In fact, of course, the winners tend to be just as full of pedigree as the mares and stallions. Otherwise, it would be only a freak piece of good fortune that made them as they are.

The stipulation for horses shown in harness and with vehicle is even less stringent. At the Shire Horse Show, for example, the animals must be of 'Shire type'. They must look like Shires, even if by some strange mutation or act of God they had been produced by a pony out of a Percheron. But it is doubtful if the magnificent specimens in those turn-outs shown by the brewers and many other trades have any but the most impeccable lineage. They are animals which, if left entire, would have done credit to the breed as stallions.

*The cross-bred*　The straight cross between two pure breeds sometimes produces an excellent animal – intelligent, robust, an example of the phenomenon known as hybrid vigour. It may also achieve a modification of a characteristic which one wants to improve or reduce in either breed. On the other hand, it may result in an animal worse in every way than both parents. A cross between two heavy breeds is normally a 'one off' production bred for a special purpose, but not to be bred from in its turn. Even for showing purposes, it is only the Shire/Clydesdale cross, in either direction, which is likely to meet with the favour of judges. Were it not for this one particular blend, we would have included cross-breds only in order to complete the tally. The Clydesdale and the Shire not only have more similarities than differences: they are in fact closely related. This intermarrying led in the late 1870s to the foundation of the stud-book societies, which promptly tried to put a stop to it. But it has continued in both directions – sometimes within the rules (in order to produce outstandingly good town draught geldings of a special type), and sometimes outside them.

*The nondescript* If your only ambition, other than work or pleasure at home, is to go to the odd carnival or fête, or perhaps to a few small shows in classes where it is your vehicle and your harness and your handling of the horse rather than the animal itself which is to be judged, or to ploughing matches and so on, you could buy a gelding of no particular blood at all.

He would scarcely be a mongrel because the stallions that had covered his female forebears were probably reputable specimens of a particular breed. Perhaps on one side or the other there was a little light-horse blood, due to someone's attempt to produce a heavyweight hunter somewhere along the line. Let us call him a mixture rather than a mongrel. You can get a lot of fun from him, especially if you learn to love him and have no illusions about him.

You could buy such a mare but not, if you are wise, for breeding. A pedigree stallion which because of his close-bred ancestry happens to be very prepotent might be able to effect a transformation, but again he might not. There is no telling, except in the pages inscribed by the Recording Angel, what amazing characteristics lie recessive in such a mare's genes, ready to create ludicrous results in the next or later generations, if some of them happen to be the ones passed on by a toss of the divine coin.

## Breed

If the Shire, Clydesdale, Suffolk and British Percheron were equally distributed throughout the country, your choice would be a matter of personal preference. None of these breeds is better than any other – and this is said in the interests of truth, not of diplomacy. (To demonstrate our impartiality, we would cheerfully add that they are the best in the world, though our transatlantic cousins might raise an objection, because they have done marvels with the breeds native to Britain and with Belgians and Percherons.) The British Percheron, for example, has become superior to the Percheron in its native France as a draught animal and as a beauty, not because we are cleverer than the French, but because they breed for meat and we still aim at motor perfection.

Nor can any of these breeds be said to be easier to handle than the others. All contain individuals that are funny-tempered, but the vast majority are extremely tractable. Your choice should be influenced by which breed is predominant in your part of the country – unless you are interested neither in breeding nor in winning prizes.

If you want a brood mare, consider where the stallions are. In

England, Shires are the most widespread. Clydesdales reign in Scotland. The Suffolk is the obvious choice if you are in or near East Anglia, and its popularity will surely grow as stallion distribution improves (as it is doing). The Percheron is, regrettably, very largely confined to Cambridgeshire and adjacent areas.

In showing, there are difficulties about exhibiting a horse of one breed in territory dominated by another. At the small shows, where all may compete together, you will find that, if you are the odd one out, your horse will have to be not only better than the others to stand top, but *much* better. Between the most prestigious shows and the humblest local ones, you will also find many which have classes for the predominant breed of the district, but none for you. Even at the Royal Show itself, you cannot possibly win with your Clydesdale, because there are classes only for the other three breeds. If you want to reach the top, are you prepared to go to the Royal Highland? But if the fun of trying to pit your Suffolk or Percheron against everyone else's Shire means more to you than collecting prizes, then go ahead. You will have a cast-iron excuse every time you do not win. And you can claim to be educating your neighbours on the virtues of a different breed.

If you care to go abroad, there is nothing except common sense to prevent your importing a foreign sort. Should you persuade someone to sell you a Frisian mare, then you are the sort of charmer who could borrow the Crown Jewels to show the kids. But, except as an object of curiosity and of private admiration, she is not going to achieve anything, either in breeding or at shows.

The only foreign heavy breed which anyone has seriously attempted to bring into this country since the Percheron was introduced in 1916 has been the Ardennes. This has much to commend it – for example, a low line of draught and docility. It is not a thing of beauty, and those who do not like it (the owners of Percherons, Suffolks, Clydesdales and Shires) say that it is obstinate rather than docile, and stupid rather than steady. They are, of course, biased, and so will you be as soon as you have a horse of your own.

*Colour*
There is an old saying that 'a good horse is never of a bad colour'. Not everyone accepts the proverb but, in the British climate, it is probably true. A good colour is the one you fancy. The one that most people fancy becomes the fashionable colour. A horse of the fashionable colour tends to command a higher price. However, you must remember that the breed societies lay down their own restrictions.

24

The Shire Society allows only black, brown, bay and grey in stallions. Chestnut, always almost universally unpopular, is now prohibited, and this beautiful colour is the sole preserve of the Suffolks. The various roans are now also banned because they are very common among Clydesdales. Chestnut or roan mares are permitted in the studbook, but frowned upon in practice.

Roans have always been a subject of argument. In the old days, some men claimed that they were all delicate, troublesome to rear and susceptible to serious diseases. Others retaliated to the effect that they were remarkably good doers, and tried to prove it by pointing to certain town stables which were almost entirely staffed by roans.

The official 'Standard of Points' for Shires states, somewhat loftily, that 'no good stallion should be splashed with large white patches over the body'. This may be assumed to mean that such a horse ought to have difficulty in persuading a Shire judge to award it a prize or a breeding premium. The reason is, again, that Clydesdales are frequently so marked.

Black always has been, and nowadays is particularly, associated with white legs, and there is no doubt that this – especially if all four legs are white to the knee or hock – is the in-colour. Bay and the darker brown are good hard colours to go for. White legs are more common accompaniments of these than they used to be.

About grey, there are differences of opinion. Some people are captivated by the beauty of some grey coats, particularly if dappled. Others are put off by the fact that grey fades with age to a sort of white, and then muck-stains are visible.

In days past, before the fetish of white legs came in, whole-colours were much favoured, particularly in stallions whose job it was to create hundreds of town geldings. You could do worse than a bay with black legs or a rich whole brown. Black on the extremities is often associated with good hard-wearing feet. In the show ring, you will probably be beaten by a horse of equal merit if it has four white legs. This is silly, but it is true.

Not surprisingly, you can buy a chestnut or roan gelding or mare cheaper than you would get an equivalent horse of another colour. You cannot make a roan coat shine. And if you breed from a roan, you might get a roan. If you breed from a chestnut, the colour may come out two, three or even five generations later, much to your son's amazement if it is too late for you to see. A 'Shire-type' might be parti-coloured, but in pedigree animals these piebalds and skewbalds were bred out long ago.

The Clydesdale may be of any colour, but roans have in recent years become extremely common, particularly the bay-roan. White on the leg has also crept ever higher. And white on the belly, noticeable in many animals a century and more ago, is even more frequent and extensive nowadays. An English horse with these characteristics may have relatives over the border, as may a Scottish one which is black or a good hard brown or bay.

The Suffolk must always be chesnut. (You will have to learn to spell it so. It is a mark of distinction. Perhaps your own name is Benet or Simson.) This is of several shades and seven used to be recognised, but in the stud-book nowadays you will find animals listed as 'red', 'dark' or 'light' chesnuts – or more commonly just 'chesnut'. Of these, the dark is least favoured, and a hundred years ago was regarded (with reason) as a sign of extraneous blood in the ancestry, especially when it was a real liver hue. It still occurs sometimes in strains where there has been no outside cross for more than a century.

Ideally, a Suffolk should have the minimum of white, and a whole-coloured animal is to be highly desired. The permitted white is chiefly confined to the face – a star or comet (star with tail on forehead); a blaze, a shim or a stripe (that is, a wide, medium or narrow mark on face); a patch on nose. On the body, white or silver hairs well blended with chesnut and insufficient to amount to anything like a roan, are allowed. White on legs is just about permissible, but much of it will not take you far.

The British Percheron stallion must be 'grey or black, with a minimum of white' – preferably no white at all. Grey is far more common in England, but in America black is favoured. You may infer that a mare might be bay or brown, but in a pure-bred animal it would be very surprising if she were. She would not win a prize, and it would be silly to breed from her.

# 2

# Spending Your Money Wisely

There is more than one way of buying your horse. The cost of its outdoor accommodation and indoor quarters will depend on what land and premises you already have or can rent. A lorry to carry it around in may be another item of initial expense, unless you prefer to pay as and if you go. We introduce these topics by urging you to acquire a money-saver in human form, and conclude them with a reminder to insure against your horse turning into a financial nightmare.

### A trusty adviser, and other help

Before you rush into a situation where sometimes even angels fear to tread, try to gain (to quote Alexander Pope twice in a single sentence) a guide, philosopher and friend. Some old retired horseman, if you can track one down, may be delighted to act in this capacity. In active life, he might have been a farmer, or a carter, or a groom. Or he might have worked in town, as a driver or stable-foreman.

There are still plenty of these people left, though not very evenly distributed. In those counties where the best horses were produced, they remain thicker on the ground than in other areas where horses were regarded simply as power-units, gladly given up and forgotten as soon as the price of a tractor could be found. The ideal person might be one who worked on a big estate where, if a man was a horseman, he was nothing else. He learned from the head man and from the other chaps, perhaps half a dozen of them, all working horses. He probably learned from his father, too. It was more or less born in them, a tradition of how to manage and understand horses.

Do your best to find such a man. He will be a treasure and a jewel. Nurture him well and let him be your Trusty Adviser. If he is a bit tottery or stiff in the joints, or if he lives some way away, he may be nothing more than this – a man to help you buy your horse, a man to be fetched occasionally so that he can tell you everything you are doing wrong. But, should he live close by and also be hale, he can be the one to step in and keep the routine going when you are away on holiday, ill in bed, or otherwise not available.

A deputy stable-hand might be, for you, so necessary (however rarely you expect him to be required) that your decision whether to buy a horse or not might depend on your ability to find such a person.

If your Trusty Adviser is unable to fill this second role, the ideal candidate, failing a perfect neighbour, might be that person whom you allow to put a pony or horse in your field. (Of this we speak later.) A business-like arrangement can enable him or her to keep an animal on your place the whole year, or at certain times of the year, for a low rent, or entirely free, in return for doing exactly what needs to be done when you require it.

### How to buy a horse

Put this off as long as you can bear to be horseless. Mix as much as you can, at shows and sales, with people who know what they are talking about. You will find some who will not tell you anything they know, and others who will. In this unexpected quarter you may find your Trusty Adviser – not a retired man at all, but one who is still active with horses and a genuine enthusiast, anxious to get someone like you off to a good start.

Listen to the practical men. Avoid the half-baked theorists and those who would fill your head with new-learned jargon. A man who has had cart-horses only a few years may be dangerous, deluding himself that he is omniscient, whereas in fact he covers a deep well of ignorance and misunderstanding with a lid of little knowledge: on the other hand, he might be humble and candid about his early mistakes, and thus help you. If you meet a man with prejudice against Suffolks, try to find another who believes they are the best horses in the world.

Look at all the horses you can, whether they are for sale or not. One has a lump on his leg. Has he had a kick? Is it an old injury? Was it done yesterday? Will it affect his usefulness? Will it disappear? You will learn a lot just by talking about a lump on a leg.

Sooner or later, you must make a firm decision about breed, sex and any particular characteristics that you desire, and the price you are prepared to pay. Put your ideas in order of priority and be prepared to forgo some points. For example, if your horse is to be a Shire, it is over-optimistic to resolve that he must be a four-year-old gelding of 18 hands, black with four white legs. Hundreds of better men than you are looking for him, too.

There are two basic ways of going about the task of actual purchase. You can buy the horse yourself. Or you can ask someone else to do it for you, which may be easier and safer.

*Buying for yourself*

When you drive out of your gates with your cheque book close to your heart, have your Trusty Adviser in the passenger seat. If he tells you not to buy a certain horse, accept his verdict. There is no need to take along a veterinary surgeon as well. He could check the horse's heart, look at its eyes, test its wind and so on. But he can only give his opinion at the time he examines the animal. You and your Trusty Adviser can look at externals, the horse static and the horse in motion. That is all that anyone can reasonably do. If you insisted on having everything vetted that you looked at, it would cost you a fortune and you might never buy anything.

Try not to go too far from home. If you live in Kent and chase up to Scotland, it will be difficult to come back empty-handed. The time and expense will seem a terrible waste, and you may be in danger of returning with something unsuitable which you would have turned down if you had gone only five miles to see it.

Auction, private owner, or dealer? Let us consider the possibilities one by one.

*Auction*    There are two sorts of auction. One is a pure horse sale run by auctioneers who specialise in this field. The other is a farm sale, usually brought about by death or retirement, which happens to include a few horses, or just one or two.

There are half-a-dozen annual or seasonal heavy-horse auctions in England and Scotland but, as the number is tending to grow, we shall not attempt to list them here, except to say that two, in the autumn, are well-known marts for Shires and Clydesdales. The Midlands Shire Foal Show and Sale is primarily, as its name suggests, for foals. You will not be wanting one of these. Clydesdales are to be found at Wigton and elsewhere, but the best generally change hands privately, as do nearly all Suffolks and Percherons. For farm auctions, you have to keep your ears open and your eyes on the agricultural and local papers.

Arrive early, choose which horses you are interested in, ask your Trusty Adviser how much you should go to for each, and then do not get carried away. Remember the quaint old custom – you are bidding in guineas, not pounds. If you successfully bid '500', that is £525. VAT at 15 per cent brings it to over £600, plus the cost of transport home.

Sometimes they do not run the animals out. At a few farm sales, they cannot do so even if they wish to, owing to congestion. That is where the expert buyer is even more at an advantage than anyone else, for he can use his intuition. You can usually ask to see a horse run out beforehand, of course. But if people hanging round know that you are interested, that might put the price up. To overcome this problem, you could get your wife or someone else to ask about the horse and see it move, while you stand quietly in the background.

You might get a warranty. This is the vendor's legally binding guarantee, either printed in the catalogue or announced by the auctioneer. Certain expressions are regularly accepted as giving or implying a warranty. For example, a 'quiet and good worker in all gears' must be able and willing to do every task that can reasonably be expected of a draught horse.

The Conditions of Sale, which must by law be exhibited and may also be printed in the catalogue, in most cases specifically define even the abbreviated expression 'quiet and good workers' in some such words as 'quiet in all gears, able to draw or back a load, sound in wind and eyes, capable of being worked, and not lame or shiverers'. ('Shivering' is a twitching of the muscles in the hindquarters which occurs when one tries to back an affected horse, an operation which in fact it will not perform because of an incurable fault in the nerves of the spinal cord.) Most Sale Conditions also state that 'broken to harness', 'used to all farm work' and 'worked up to date of sale' are warranties and that horses so described must be quiet and capable of being worked.

The Conditions normally say that descriptions of height or age do not constitute a warranty. And, in the case of horses which realise less than a stated sum, any warranty is deemed to be void.

Any sort of *partial* warranty may be useless. Normally, if something is omitted, it is not through oversight. For example, 'has been worked in chains' (see Chapter 6, page 121) may be true: but it does not say when, how often, with what success or why the horse is unacquainted with other gears. He may have had chains on once, five years ago, and after two minutes accelerated to forty miles an hour, smashing up everything in his path, since when no one has dared to interfere with his life of permanent leisure.

Subjective epithets like 'staunch' or 'upstanding' are not warranties. Is the horse staunch in his resistance to work? Are not all horses upstanding except when they are lying down? What a horse 'may make' or 'will be' is nothing more than the vendor's pious hope and should be ignored. But 'quiet in traffic' is different. If you buy a horse so described and he shies at the paper-boy's bike and takes wing when the vicar's car approaches, there has been a breach of warranty.

If a horse does not fulfil the warranty, you have only a short time, usually up to 7 pm the following day (unless that happens to be a Sunday), to return him, or, if you are at a distance, to telephone the auctioneer. Beyond that limit, you have no redress. So test him as soon as you get him home, and if he does not come up to the stated standard, ring at once and send him back as soon as you can. The auctioneer will appoint a third person to test him. The losing party pays the fee for this and keeps the horse.

If the horse you buy is 'warranted sound', you are supposed to have him examined on the spot by a veterinary surgeon if you suspect that he is not so, because a certificate of soundness is, obviously, valid only at the moment of signature. (By the time you get a sound horse home, he might be unsound. Bad luck.) If, however, he is a crib-biter or wind-sucker (this silly habit of gulping air into the stomach causes indigestion and therefore unsoundness), you cannot be expected to detect it until you are home, and so the normal day's grace is given.

Should your vet discover an infirmity or disease which in his opinion is of long standing and was indubitably present at the time of sale, you can send the horse back with a certificate to this effect, if there was a warranty implying soundness. If the vendor disputes it, an independent veterinary inspection will be carried out, all expenses being paid by the losing party. This situation, of course, is highly unlikely to arise if the vendor actually supplied a veterinary certificate in the first place, since no one is likely to certify a horse sound when he is not.

Some auctions discourage warranties because of the time and trouble caused by disputes. Many vendors prefer not to make any claim for animals which are not fully earning their living; and, in a world dominated by distrust, some are honest to the point of naivety. Therefore, 'has been in chains' may in fact disguise no evil at all, but mean simply that the horse has been very little used. The situation is confusing.

Your chief grounds for suspicion arise when the vendor hides behind a cloak of anonymity. If a horse is offered as 'the property of a gentleman', what assurance is that supposed to give? That its stable or table manners are good? It is possibly a 'wrong 'un' and the term 'gentleman' would be judged a breach of warranty in the heavenly courts.

You will probably not make a purchase at your first sale, but you might at your fourth or fifth. By then, you will be more knowledgeable – and poorer, especially if you travel some distance and have to stay overnight in hotels. Also it will be years before you are competent to go on your own and buy the right horse at the right price. You may therefore decide it is cheaper and better to buy privately.

*Private purchase*   If you are honest with him, a private owner will generally be willing to show you his horses. On the other hand, he will not be happy wasting hours with nosey parkers wishing to fill in a spare half-day. But if you are going to buy a horse one day, he would not want to deter you from coming to him.

You will not get a warranty this way. Instead, you will have to ask to see the horse actually doing the various classes of work and then judge for yourself. If the owner pays his horse marvellous compliments, do not ask him to write them down. This is tantamount to saying you believe he is a crook and you will be lucky not to be thrown off the premises. Nor must you say anything else to suggest that you distrust him. There was one prospective buyer who insistently repeated his questions, explaining 'I was done once before, you see'. Even if you think the owner is trying to 'do' you, it is better to meet lies with courteous excuses than to be so offensive as this.

Far too many would-be buyers make the elementary error of accepting an invitation to a meal or to stay the night with a potential vendor. He will possibly show you an animal that exactly meets your stated requirements. He knows all about horses and your knowledge is very little. You may have absolutely no reason for turning it down – except that, somehow, you just do not like it. If you are under the slightest social obligation to your host, you will now be in an embarrassing situation. It might be added that not everyone has such delicate feelings. Some people, having heard of the fabled hospitality of heavy-horse men, even have the nerve to ask if they can come to lunch before seeing the horses, though they have never met the vendor.

On the other hand, do not be put off by the appearance of any place you visit. The best horses are often to be found in the mud. The successful man is the one who can recognise a good horse in bad surroundings and in bad condition.

Buying and selling horses is a matter of two-way trust. Do not try to be clever – if you are a mug, a horseman will know at once. So admit that you are a beginner, but do not blurt out that you have £x to spend. The owner will inevitably just happen to have a really good horse that he had not intended to sell, but which he might be prepared to let go. It is worth more than the figure you mentioned, but to give you a good start he would let you have it for £x + y. The size of y will depend on how silly he judges you to be. If he actually believes £x is your real maximum, he might even quote £x − y. You will buy and be grateful, until it dawns on you that this is a horse he would have been glad to get rid of for two-thirds the price you paid.

Let your Trusty Adviser know how much you can spend. When a figure is quoted for a particular horse, he can shake his head or give you the nod. You can then begin a bit of honest bargaining, saying that, much as you like the horse, you cannot manage more than £x. See how you go from there. A reasonable man will be prepared to take the horse back if it does not suit. This is better than any warranty, but do not try to take advantage of it. Ring him up within a couple of days, not after two months.

When you have done a deal, try to make a friend and ally of the vendor. He wants you to be happy. You may after all come back for another animal, and you will certainly recommend him to your friends. It is amazing how generous people can be. There was one case where a well-established man sold a filly to a young farmer for breeding. She just would not oblige, but at the time of the sale no one could have known. A few years later, the breeder let his youthful customer have another horse at a ridiculously low price. There are still people like that.

If you buy privately in response to an advertisement, the situation is different. In the first place, why did the man advertise at all? It is easy enough to make a quick sale of a cart-horse at a fair price, without the expense of advertising. And secondly, the vendor is approaching you, as a member of the public. You have not applied to him, and have therefore no duty to assume that he is honest. Study the advertisement carefully, because a warranty might be involved.

If there is and you are sold a pup instead of a horse, write at once to explain in what respects the horse fails to match the description. Should the vendor refuse to admit his error, or fail to reply, write no more but speak to your solicitor instead. Unfortunately, you will be in for a worrying and perhaps expensive time. A breach of warranty will entitle you in this case only to damages, unless the warranty is actually (as at auctions) a condition of sale entitling you to repudiate the deal, or unless the Misrepresentation Act 1967 (or, if the vendor sells horses as a trade or business, the Trade Descriptions Act 1968) can help you. Amidst all this, the chief beneficiary will probably be your solicitor.

Be particularly suspicious of an expression like 'reasonable price to good home'. This might be (in the words adopted by auctioneers) 'calculated to deceive purchasers' by conjuring up the image of an animal-lover who would fainer sell his grandmother than his horse to a bad home.

*Dealer* By this term we do not mean a shifty, shady individual who, if he has a fixed abode, does not reveal it to you or meet you there. We speak of a man whose address and number are in the telephone book, who has probably been established a number of years and whose house and premises give every appearance of solid comfort, if not affluence.

How is he doing so well? Certainly not by swindling his customers. He buys horses whose history he often does not know and about whose soundness and temperament he has to make his own judgment. He feeds and houses them, and schools them if necessary, until such time as customers buy them. If that interval is too long, his stock-in-trade will have eaten up all his profit. He must give his clients not only an honest deal, but a deal which suits them. One sale which does not please the customer will be detrimental to his reputation.

He must know all about horses and a lot about people. His most difficult client is likely to be you – the beginner. Many people are frank about their ignorance of music or painting, and even boast of it, but few will admit how little they know of horses. So beginners often obstruct the dealer by pretending to be more competent than they really are. He will not sell you an unsuitable horse unless you deceive him into doing so, for that is bad business. Nor will he set out to cheat you, but if you try to act big when he knows that horse-wise you are small it might afford him a giggle to charge you £50 more than the horse is worth.

Years ago, many dealers specialised in cart-horses and, if you called at the right time, you could choose from a yard full of them. But today you would not expect a dealer to keep even one 'on spec', as he keeps cobs and hunters: and the heavy-horse trade is so largely conducted by private sale and auction that he may not even have handled one recently. You might have to place an order with him, in which case you will do better if you can find some heavy-horse man who will buy on your behalf.

### Asking someone to buy for you

A man who keeps horses in a fairly big way will know where all the other ones are, for miles around. He will also know other men, all over the country perhaps, who will know where many more horses are. Among all these, there will be just the horse for you, available for purchase, and at the right price.

If you can discover such a man, who is also an honest and friendly sort of fellow, get to know him. (You will soon be pointed in his direction by recommendation – and perhaps warned against getting involved with certain other gentlemen, too.) Ask him if he would be willing to look out for a horse on your behalf. Tell him the price you can pay and discuss fully the sort of animal you desire. He will want to be quite certain that there is going to be no mistake. Finally, you must trust him implicitly.

If you are surprised by what he produces, accept what he has done for you. It is futile to tell him you expected a shiny black when he produces a muddy bay. Unless you have failed to give the specifications properly in the first place, it will be the right horse for you. Remember that you asked him to buy you a horse and he has done so and you now owe him the money. Furthermore, he will have already incurred plenty of expense and spent perhaps a lot of time on your behalf. Common sense suggests that, when talking of your ceiling price in the first place, you introduce this point – a delicate way of giving him the opportunity of showing that, very reasonably, he expects to make a pound or so out of the affair. You will not know, of course, whether in any case he will add a bit to what he pays the vendor.

Many established horsemen put their expertise to advantage by buying and selling and he may therefore really be buying for you on commission. This would still be an excellent arrangement and perhaps less embarrassing than if he brushed aside the sordid subject of money in a vague or gentlemanly manner. But if he really does seem to be acting for you as a genuine favour, remember the enormous sum of money it would have cost you to go rushing round the country looking for a suitable horse, and give him a present.

Do not ask more than one man at a time. This advice may appear so obvious as to be superfluous, but common sense seems to desert many people when they are looking for a horse. If you approach several people, the news will probably get round, and those best placed to help you will lose interest. Alternatively, two of them may each produce a horse so that one will be left with an animal on his hands which he does not want and which no one else is likely to want either.

## Land

You cannot keep a cart-horse without some grass for him to run about on (unless of course he is to be a town work-horse taking sufficient daily exercise on his job to make it reasonable for him to stay indoors throughout his free time). Land adjoining your house and garden will obviously make life easier than a field some two miles away.

You ought to own or rent two or three acres: for two horses, say six acres. The more you have, the better. It will enable you to keep extra horses eventually, if things go well. In the meantime, your horse will be happier if there is enough land for him to share with your children's ponies or with those of someone else. Horses are not solitary animals and love company. There could be a distinct advantage to you in allowing someone else to keep a horse or pony or two on your land, if that someone is sensible and reliable, as we have already mentioned.

If your land is all in one piece, divide it up into two or, better, three paddocks, or even four if you can. Eight acres arranged in four more or less equal parts could be ideal. Horses get tired of staying in the same place all the time, and it is not good to school them where they live. The land gets 'tired', too. Worse than that, it harbours those parasites which are peculiar to the equine species, and rotation of grazing is a vital ploy in combating them.

You may have a hedge, or hedges. If these are good, that is fine; but they are no use unless they can be guaranteed to keep your horse in, and not to do him any harm. You will have to put up fencing for your sub-divisions, and perhaps at weak or unsatisfactory points in the hedges as well.

If you have to erect something yourself, or if there is some fencing there already and you are wondering whether it is suitable, there are four types to consider:

1. *post and rail*   This looks the nicest, but is very expensive, and has to be in top-class condition. Wood can splinter, which is dangerous; also wood is attractive to horses for rubbing and leaning against. It

must therefore be strong enough to withstand considerable pressure.

2. *barbed wire*   This is unsightly, but will keep a cart-horse in and he will have a healthy respect for it. But it must be kept really taut, and be of four strands – not just two. The top wire must be at least as high as the tops of his legs, and preferably half-way up his chest. Settle for a height of 4ft 6in. The lower strands can be of plain wire if you like.

3. *plain wire*   This may seem less barbarous (which is not intended as a pun), but can present a far greater hazard. Although to the horse it may not look formidable, it can cut like cheese-wire if he charges it, because it is no good at all unless tightly drawn. Another drawback is that your horse will push against it, because it does not hurt, in order to eat some inviting grass on the other side. Soon the whole fence will be a pathetic sight, sagging badly and proving dangerous rather than useless.

4. *electric fence*   This has definite advantages for it gives you the opportunity to alter very easily the shape and size of your individual paddocks. Such a fence run off the mains, which is the best method, will keep even a stallion in – even if there are mares about, and there can be no higher testimonial. But there is always the worry that the current might go off or that the fence will earth itself. In such a situation, the horse will soon find out, usually before you do. Occasionally, therefore, it might be a good idea to push the wire into him with a stick, to remind him what a nasty thing it is. (He will not associate you as the prime cause with the effect, and will not bear a grudge.) You cannot strain an electric fence taut, but it must be well supported. A drooping fence run off a nearly flat battery is a hazardous combination.

The most terrifying aspect of a horse getting out, these days, is traffic on a road. The law is very complicated and confusing in apportioning liability for accidents of mixed motor traffic and horses. If your horse is not in his field, then it is the lawyers who may have a field day. Steer clear of the law regarding the highway. If we wanted to put you off the idea of keeping a horse, we would concentrate on two main topics – worms and the law. Your horse cannot avoid worms, but you must avoid the law.

In contemplating your fences, consider the mentality of your horse and of the public at large. The latter is easier, because it is only the idiot fringe you have to worry about. Try to think what harm could be done by careless (or, sadly, malevolent) people, including those who have no right on your land. If a gate is easily opened, especially one giving access to a road or a field of strawberries, padlock it. You must provide a stile, of course, if there is a public right of way.

Your cart-horse will however be easier to keep within bounds than, say, a New Forest pony, which is born free and is an amazingly tough animal. These ponies have been known to charge a barbed-wire fence and knock it flat without coming to harm. A Thoroughbred would probably be severely injured. So might a cart-horse: but then he would not charge a barbed-wire fence. Nevertheless, study your own horse's mind, so that you will not be taken by surprise. His thinking and behaviour will not necessarily be the same as that of others, even his brother.

An excellent fence is not much good if there is a rickety gate. And a good gate can become rickety if it is daily leaned against by the rear end of a cart-horse, with all his weight in front of it. So it is wise to add a strand of barbed wire to any gate, on the inside of the top rail. Horses love to have a good rub, but should not be encouraged to demolish a gate gradually.

Of course, your horse is expected to eat the grass, as well as run about on it. What sort of greenery grows in your paddock? Do not assume, because much of the vegetation has grown so high that you can hardly see him, that 'He's got plenty of grass'. See whether there are patches which he has grazed short. Those areas contain the herbage he likes, and he would sooner die than eat the other trash. How much of his living your horse can get off his paddocks depends more on what grows on them than on how big they are. If they are an old bit of heath on top of a mountain, you will have to feed him a lot. If they are rich grazing land, he will get as fat as butter on nothing else during the summer.

If you decide to try and make hay from the edges and the scrappy bits of your paddocks, sell it for what it is: pretty poor stuff. Someone will want it for their cattle, and the price you get can be set off against the cost of some good hay. Of course, this does not apply if you have plenty of ground and some can be reserved, after an early bite, entirely for hay. Even then it is not going to be of much use if it is merely rough old pasture with a lot of rubbish and coarse grass in it.

Move your horses round in rotation from paddock to paddock and, if possible, get a local farmer to put in some heifers or steers behind them for short periods, to clean up what the horses will not touch. Let him do it for nothing, if necessary, for it is to your advantage. If every paddock can have a complete rest from horses for two-thirds of the year or for three-quarters (with a weekly move in spring and summer, but less frequent at other times), then you will do much to control the activities of worms, those foes already hinted at and to be discussed later.

To keep the land in good general condition, you should chain-harrow in spring and roll after it has been cut up during the winter. There is no need to pick up the droppings, though you can do so if you have a mind: but it is better to harrow again as soon as each paddock is empty of stock. You can get someone to put on a bit of fertiliser, but do not put your horses back in any of the paddocks until there has been a good shower of rain. If your land is suitable, you can have each paddock ploughed up in rotation every few years and reseeded (see Chapter 3, page 49).

It is a good idea to ask a local farmer or a contractor to advise on any weed problems. If you spray, read the instructions carefully. The manufacturers may advise you not to put your animals in the treated area for six weeks. In that case, do not try it after five, just to see if they survive. And watch out for spraying being done by your neighbour in the next field. Horses have died this way – and it does not mean that the other chap has been particularly careless or inconsiderate. Spray drifts in the breeze in a surprising manner.

Look out for things that might poison your horse. You are unlikely to have a yew growing in the field or hedge, and even more unlikely to keep him in the churchyard. But make sure there is no deadly nightshade, nor bracken or ragwort or foxglove, though you would have to starve your horse pretty drastically before he would voluntarily poison himself with these. It is improbable that he will imagine he is a pig and eat a lot of acorns, which are marvellous for growing tasty bacon but noxious to horses. Do not let him wander into an area infested by adders, to whose bite he will be particularly sensitive.

If your horse is unfortunately poisoned, it is more likely to be due to your grossly over-administering otherwise useful medicine, or carelessly using weed-killers (you really *must* read what it says on that can), or giving him mouldy food or impure water. He will poison himself only if he has no good food available and is desperately hungry. But he cannot help himself if you give him four times the recommended dose of medicine.

Should you have a gate leading to a public road, you must not only guard against its being left open. People will love to feed your horse. If you find him shaking his head furiously about, it could be (as on one occasion it was) that someone has just given him a ham sandwich, spread thickly with mustard. Really, you do not want your horse fed by anyone but yourself. Nor is it just a matter of health. If strangers bring him good things, he will expect to be fed tit-bits on sight – and by you, too. He will take a step forward, with perhaps a cart behind him, just to see if you are going to be a softie also. Other people can make a horse a perfect pest to his owner.

If you are in semi-surburban surroundings, beware the person who tips large amounts of lawn-mowings over the hedge – 'lovely grass for the horse'. If they fall in a heap and he eats them after they have had time to begin heating, they will blow him up and kill him as quickly as any expensive poison.

A road running alongside your land can bring other hazards. Even though councils now provide public tips, there are still people who will present you with their valueless antiques. Mattress springs for your horse to entangle his feet; perfectly palatable grass growing through the mass of tiny wires from a burnt-out tyre which will perforate his insides; bits of plastic to give him a stoppage; broken bottles to cut him – all these are unwanted gifts, but they still arrive. Even if the local council allows you to erect a large notice DO NOT FEED THIS HORSE or THIS ANIMAL IS DANGEROUS, it will be treated as a challenge rather than a warning, so you need to keep a wary eye at all times.

Do not forget water. A trough (which can be an old bath) can serve two paddocks if correctly sited. A clean stream is ideal, if it really is clean and does not have a sandy bottom. A regular intake of sand will kill your horse in the end, though it may take years. With polythene piping you can easily lay on a water supply so there is no excuse for its not being fresh. But do not forget that water can freeze.

Finally, it is nice for the horse to have a bit of shelter, whether from the sun or the wind or the rain. A field shelter can be arranged to serve two paddocks. There is no need to lay a concrete base, but do not erect the shelter in a hollow which will be filled with water in a rainy season. Throw some straw down to make a pleasant place to stand. If there is a suitable tree in the field, he may enjoy standing under that.

## Housing

You must have some sort of a building for your horse, for three reasons: to give him shelter when he needs it; to give yourself a place where you can tie him up, groom him, examine his feet, put his

A stall showing manger, hay-rack and salt-lick. See also the halter, chog and tie-ring. This stall is 6ft 6in by 8ft

harness on, have him shod and so on; to provide an area where his feed can be placed and not spoil.

The absolute essentials about this building are that it should be dry, well ventilated, and yet free from draughts. If he is provided with these conditions, your horse will thrive. He does not require central heating, for he is happy in temperatures which would not please us at all. For a cart-horse, you will not even need a stable rug.

The same building (or one nearby) will have to contain storage space for bedding – up to two tons; hay; other foods; harness; grooming kit; medicines; and cleaning tools. Dry and airy conditions are also needed for these.

Your tack room and stores are obviously most convenient if adjacent to, or part of, the stable building. Also the nearer both field and buildings are to your house, the better for you. If you have to rent a field half a mile away, you cannot keep an eye on things all the time. And, however well equipped the accommodation, you would not wish to risk keeping your harness there.

You may be lucky and have some buildings in the right position which can be adapted. You might even have one that once actually was a stable, and there might be little to do except clean it up and replace the missing fittings. If your horses will be working regularly, stalls are good. Otherwise, and especially to house one horse, a loose box is the answer. It should not measure less than 14ft by 12ft.

If you are going to have to start from scratch, remember to check whether you need planning permission. Remember also that, if you move, you cannot take it with you so the better you build, the more the value of your property is enhanced.

Whether you build to the highest standard or more modestly, you will want a concrete floor, a water supply, and, if possible, electricity for lighting and for heating water to clean your horse. Above the concrete base, the ideal surface is a floor of Staffordshire blue bricks. The walls, to match this splendid foundation, should be of good-quality building bricks. There should be a damp course and the roof should be insulated to prevent condensation.

For a more modest and cheaper structure, the floor can be left as concrete, with the walls composed of concrete blocks. All the bottom layers should consist of blocks laid flat, to give maximum thickness. Just by pushing his backside against them, a heavy horse can eventually crack a concrete block if it is laid wrongly. The upper layers can of course be laid upright. All doors should be at least 4ft wide.

If you wish to keep within the lowest possible outlay, you might be aiming to just knock something up yourself. This is all right – if you provide the concrete base. But it is no good to use 2in by 2in battens and the cheapest walling material. A loose box should not be so loose that it soon becomes S-shaped so the boards must be 1in not ½in thick. Marine plywood is excellent stuff, and spreads the shock of a kick. Remember that your horse will not merely lean heavily against the walls: he will at times kick them.

This loose box is 14ft by 12ft. You can see the manger, hay-rack and tie-ring. Notice the protective mesh on the window

In planning your stabling, especially when erecting it as a DIY job, do consider the horse's safety. Nowhere should there be any sharp corners or sharp edges to brickwork. If you leave any such hazard, it will cause trouble sooner or later. Horses will injure themselves in the simplest and, apparently, the most idiotic way – getting a foot caught under a bit of galvanised tin, for instance, and sustaining a bad cut. Think ahead for your horse as you would for a small child or an elderly person, and make sure that a protruding rusty nail is removed before he punctures himself on it.

Of course, instead of erecting a permanent building, you may decide to buy a custom-built wooden loose box, of the right size for a cart-horse. You can also buy a harness room to go with it. If you move house, you can of course take this portable stabling with you, but, if possible, sell it with the house and buy a new one at the other end.

However, do not worry too much about appearances. Do the best you can, according to your means and any other restrictions. Your horse needs dry and ventilated quarters, big enough, and free from draughts and dangers. If you have doubts or problems, get your Trusty Adviser along to help you picture in your mind's eye your daily routine once the horse is installed, and eliminate all inconveniences that are not absolutely unavoidable.

## Transport

If you are often going to take your horse all over the place and you have plenty of money, then there is no practical problem – you can buy a lorry of your own. Do not forget you will have to obtain an HGV licence if you propose to drive it yourself. (Another little point about driving your own lorry is that finding diesel can be difficult on Saturday nights and Sundays. Have a full tank as the week-end approaches.)

A 16ft cattle lorry will take three cart-horses, or two horses and a plough (or harrow or cultivator), or one horse and a cart. The implement must go at the front and the horse or horses at the back, to give you some chance of saving the animals should the lorry catch fire or if there is an accident. By law, the horses must also be partitioned off from the dead stock – otherwise, in the event of an emergency stop, they will come to grief through being thrown on to the machinery. If the load is composed entirely of horses, those at the back must of course be partitioned off from those in front.

Horses are supposed to stand lengthways in the vehicle, which is also common sense. A few prefer to travel with their rumps to the engine, which seems odd. Each horse should be tied to its side of the lorry. A foal of course should travel with its mother. Be wary of transporting a strange animal alongside one of your own. Some horses will take an instant dislike to another and behave very nastily. You do not want to travel a hundred miles with one horse attempting to attack its travelling companion throughout the journey.

Alternatively, if you want to take a waggon with you, you might consider buying a smaller lorry, suitable for just two horses, and a trailer with a winch on it. You will then use the trailer only when you need to do so, which seems a good idea, except that you will find you cannot do without it even if it is only a plough you need to take. Incidentally, in your concern for your horses' welfare, do not omit to ensure that, if you are transporting a plough, it is secured firmly for travelling. The metal is cast, and is liable to smash to smithereens.

If you have not the money to buy your own lorry, or if you are going to only a couple of shows a year, and not far away at that, then obviously you will be thinking of a contractor to take you about. This is hideously expensive, mainly because of the driver's wages. Unfortunately, self-drive hiring does not seem to have really come on to the animal-transport scene. It is not regarded as good business so, although this may seem a bright idea, you must forget it.

There are two types of men who drive lorries. If you are unlucky, you will get one who regards you as a nuisance. He is the sort who spends most of his week driving cattle, sheep or pigs unsympathetically fast, relying on their being herded tightly together to ensure that there will be only a couple of unfortunates on the floor, underneath the rest, when they reach their destination. He does not understand horses, nor does he have any wish to do so. He will ignore, or regard as fussy, your reminders that horses have to stand independently, on their own four legs, when travelling. Apart from driving badly, he will do nothing else for you. He will sit in his cab while you unload, and again when you load up. If he does not like getting home late, he will make it so plain that you will leave the show earlier than you wish, just to keep the peace. And he will find other ways to ruin completely your day out.

Conversely, you may have the pleasure of finding a chap who not only appreciates your intention to enjoy the day, but is prepared to do so himself and he will take a real interest in what you are up to. He may love heavy horses and actually be glad to lend a hand. If you win a prize, let him share the joy. With any luck, he will become as 'involved' as you are. Ask for him again the next time, and hope that another customer has not already done so.

Another idea well worth exploring is the possibility of sharing with a lorry owner who has room in his vehicle for your horse as well as his own. If you strike up such an arrangement as this, you will naturally have to offer something more realistic than filling up the tank with diesel to start with and its owner with beer afterwards.

Or you might borrow a vehicle. In this case, you must remember that there are strict requirements embodied in the Transport of Animals Act for those vehicles which carry animals and these regulations must be strictly adhered to.

Best of all, you might have a friend with a suitable vehicle who does not normally take animals to shows and who would love to team up with you for a good day out, especially if you paid all expenses. You never know your luck.

## Insurance

Whereas the law requires you to insure your motor vehicle against any claims that may be brought against you, it does not compel you to take similar precautions in respect of your horse. You are at liberty to take him, uninsured, where you will. If with a crippling kick he ends some promising young man's career and the judge awards colossal damages which you cannot possibly pay, the sufferer's plight will be added to the shame of your own bankruptcy.

Insurance companies, ever realistic, regard the likelihood of your horse maiming or killing anyone as pretty remote, for they will cheerfully cover you against third-party liability up to half a million pounds, either as part of a comprehensive policy or for a mere extra couple of pounds or so. In fact, they generously promise to pay up 'for every incident' or 'on each occasion', though their sunny nature would be doubtless dimmed if your horse always ran amok at shows and slew or disabled someone once a week. But even if the chances of such a thing happening only once are regarded as less likely than your winning a vast fortune on the pools, some people do win vast fortunes on the pools.

The misfortunes that more commonly exercise the minds of insurers are those which might befall your horse, rather than any he might originate. The basic cover in most policies provides against his death from any cause (including foaling in the case of a mare) and loss by theft or straying. The premium applicable to a cart-horse (perhaps as little as 2.5 per cent) is much lower than for a horse engaged in, say, point-to-point racing (possibly 6 per cent). If you wish also to be fully covered against his being permanently incapacitated, either through accident, illness or disease, it might cost you something over 4 per cent. Humane slaughter, unless the reason is one of those specifically mentioned in the policy, will require the company's written agreement. It is obviously essential to insure your horse for his full value.

Most standard quotations are for horses aged thirty days to fifteen years, though a veterinary certificate will be required for animals over twelve or valued at more than a stated sum. For those which are sixteen years old or more, a higher premium will, not surprisingly, be payable. You will in any case have to make a declaration about your horse's present condition and recent history. Take care that you not only answer the questions honestly but also reveal any additional matters which the insurers ought to know. 'Uberrima fides' is the lawyers' expression to denote the 'absolute faith' that is expected to exist between you and the insurance company.

If you wish to insure against liability for veterinary fees incurred through accidental injury or illness, look carefully at the terms. Operations not simply to save the life of your horse will require the insurers' prior written agreement, and an additional premium may be payable. In all cases of accident or illness likely to result in a claim, call your vet promptly and notify the company at once. The latter will rely on the veterinary report and will also want to be certain that the proper course of action is taken. They will wish to be satisfied, too, that you have been looking after your horse properly – feeding him right, treating him for worms, and so on. Dark suspicions about this sort of thing are more likely to arise here than in a policy on the life of, say, your spouse. No one will insure you against foaling costs or for protective inoculations.

You may feel that the cover available under a horse policy against personal accident to yourself is inadequate, or it may not even be available. Your present personal policy may already protect you, or may be adjusted to do so. Insurance of harness against theft, fire or accident is another matter which you might prefer to add to an existing policy, and the same applies of course to vehicles, implements and your new stabling. There is no point in taking out a 'comprehensive' policy if that means paying for cover which is irrelevant or, conversely, if it does not really comprehend all your horse's proposed activities. If, for example, you use your horse for trade, you will almost certainly have to take out more than one policy to meet all your needs, both in the matter of public liability during all the operations involved in using the streets and in delivering and collecting goods and for your own protection against damage to vehicles and harness.

Horse insurance is a specialised business, but you should have no trouble in finding the right company and the right policy. If you are a farmer and a member of the NFU, it is easy: ask your NFU representative. If you belong to your breed society, the secretary will put you in touch with a broker who is an expert in this branch of insurance; you might be able to get favourable rates under a group scheme. Otherwise, ask your own broker or scan the pages of the equine press.

One thing you will be unable to do is to restrict your cover to third-party liability – at least, for the economical sum mentioned earlier. Insurance companies fix a minimum premium per animal and in practice would want you to take out a policy on your horse's life first, before giving protection against the terrifying, if improbable, risk of incurring damages, in the twinkling of an eye or the whizz of a hoof, to the tune of half a million pounds.

# 3

# Basic Creature Comforts

You have your horse. He has somewhere to live. What next? Something to eat and something to drink; a good bed; and a clean skin. These are our daily needs, and his.

### Feeding

*Pasture* is of course the horse's natural source of food. This should be permanent pasture, which contains scores of different grasses and hundreds of other species of plant as well. Good grazing contains in bounteous profusion everything to provide a balanced diet, and the horse, which has a sophisticated palate, is perfectly capable of deciding what he requires. He cannot explain to you why he selects certain things and leaves others, but he instinctively knows what he is doing. So do not be surprised if he browses sometimes in the hedge and starts eating shoots and leaves and bark. Even if you spot him eating a lump of soil, do not worry.

If you plough up any of your pasture for re-seeding, you should therefore re-sow with a special all-sorts mixture recommended for the job by your seedsman. Leys, consisting of a limited number of pure grasses, are both boring and inadequate for your horse. The herbage on limestone is better for a horse's bone-formation than any other, but you can scarcely move to the other side of the country just to get it.

The cart-horse is not native to our soil. His evolution has been tampered with by man, so that he is unnaturally huge and strong. He cannot subsist in a state of good health all the year round on even perfect pasture. In the winter, therefore, and also according to what extent you withdraw him from pasture in summer, and – particularly – in order to compensate for the work you take out of him at various times, he will need feeding by you.

The food that he is given can constitute any proportion of the total requirement, up to 100 per cent. The great brewery horses eat nothing

49

either on working days or at week-ends that is not given to them. So do not worry if your fields are poor, or even if they consist of little more than dusty exercise-grounds. It simply means that your feed-bill will be greater than it would be if some of his needs could be met by grazing. Provided you can give him sufficient exercise, in the form of work or otherwise, he can still thrive if you have no fields at all.

Here are ten principles of feeding:

1. Most cart-horses nowadays are underworked, or even idle. Therefore, their greatest peril, particularly in the hands of a novice, is overfeeding. The worst enemy of an idle horse is fodder which would be suitable to him if he were working. The worst enemy of a horse in light work is fodder which would be right if he were toiling hard and long. The worst enemy of a horse working spasmodically is to be fed on rest days the same rations as he needs on working days. Although modern man can miraculously survive the constant serious abuse of his digestive system by gross over-feeding, especially of rich foods, and sluggish under-exercise, the horse is so constituted that he cannot accept this.

2. Every horse has its own special requirements. Obviously, these depend partly on its age; its size; the season of the year; the availability and quality of pasture; and similar factors. But in addition, two apparently identical horses leading identical lives may have different needs – different quantities, and different proportions of ingredients – to keep them at their best. One may be a shy feeder and the other have a healthy appetite. Every horse must therefore be treated as an individual.

3. Water him before feeding, not after. Good wholesome, clean fresh *water* is essential to life. He should have access to this at all times – with two exceptions. If he is very hot and sweaty after hard work, he should not be allowed to drink much cold water until he has really cooled down. And he should not be watered soon after a feed, particularly if it contains a concentrated food such as oats. In either case, he might develop colic. Otherwise, he should drink as often as he wants, consuming anything up to ten gallons some days.

4. Feed your horse at the same time every day. If he is in work, three times at least: morning, mid-day and evening. If he is idle, the mid-day feed can be omitted. If he has not finished up his last meal by the time you arrive with the next one, you are overdoing it – unless he is going off his feed because he is sickening for an illness, or there is

something wrong with what you have given him, or he happens to have dunged in his manger. In his natural surroundings, he spends a considerable part of each twenty-four hours eating, like all grazers and browsers, but his stomach can take only a limited amount at any one time. So he eats intermittently. 'Little and often' is therefore the motto, and so it would be better to increase his feeds to four a day rather than reduce them to one as long as the total quantity is not thereby increased.

5. Give him only good quality fodder, and clean. This is not just a matter of health but of economy too. If forage is mouldy or dusty, he will waste as much as he eats.

6. The foundation of good feeding in the stable is hay.

7. All concentrated feeds should be measured by the pound weight. While you are still learning, it is a good idea to record what foods you have fed, and their weights, so that you can adjust according to circumstances. Then, if you have to hand over the job for a day or two to someone else, you can leave precise instructions.

8. Horses like a bit of superficial variety, but do not suddenly and radically change his basic diet. You will do him a lot of harm that way. A pig or other omnivore, especially a human, can survive an incredible difference of foodstuffs from one meal to the next or from today to tomorrow. But not a horse. Even a new sort of hay should not be abruptly introduced. If your old supply is running out and your new lot is a quite different kind, it would be wise to mingle the new with the old gradually instead of making a complete change on a Wednesday evening or Thursday morning.

9. Allow at least an hour, and preferably two, to elapse after feeding, before you begin to work your horse.

10. *Salt* should be available to your horse at all times, in the form of a mineral lick or, if you can get it, rock salt.

So much for principles. Now to particulars. Let us consider the most common feeding stuffs.

*Hay*   As our sixth principle stated, hay is the foundation of good feeding. It is good roughage and a good subsistence diet. Seeds hay is the best. Clover hay is also all right, and a little more laxative, but not much is grown nowadays. Hay must be of the finest quality you can get, and properly made. When you open the bale it should smell delicious – just like hay! If it is too dry and crumbly, it has little value. If dust flies out, it is mouldy. If it has gone a dark colour, it was made too quickly and has heated. Badly made hay not only fails as a feeding stuff, but can do a lot of harm – if your horse condescends to eat it, which he probably will not. Hay in good condition, but made from coarse rubbish, remains what it was before it was made: rubbish.

*Chaff*  You can feed hay 'long' – as it is; or 'short' – chopped up with a chaff-cutter, which is so named because short hay is called chaff or chop. The quality must be no less good. You can include a certain amount of chopped oat straw if you like, but it is then less nutritious. Chaff is particularly useful when mixed with oats or other concentrated and high-energy feeding stuffs, as it adds bulk and ensures better mastication by slowing down the horse's rate of eating.

*Broad bran* is good for the digestion and also gives bulk to the oat ration. It is not so easy to get, and expensive. Its second use, and an important one, is as a mash, which is mildly laxative and is also good for sick horses. In this form it was fed to town horses in the old days on Saturdays to keep their bowels open during the somnolent Sabbath, and the same religion is good working practice today. To make a bran mash, fill a stable bucket about two-thirds full of bran. Stir in enough freshly boiled water to make it thoroughly wet (but not sloppy), and cover with a sack until cool. A good mash will be 'crumble dry' when touched. A tablespoonful of salt will make it more palatable, and it should be served fresh.

*Oats*  If we turn now to the more powerful feed stuffs, oats are the standard high-energy concentrated feed, suitable for horses doing hard or fast work. They should be fed with great caution and mixed with a bulky feed, as they are over-heating for a horse doing little work. Too little is a less dangerous error than too much.

Oats should be crushed. Though your horse is capable of crunching them up to tiny digestible morsels if his teeth are all right, he will probably be too impatient. It is a waste of money as well as of nourishment, and deleterious to the digestive system, if they come out at the other end with their goodness not properly absorbed into the body. You will no doubt buy them ready crushed, and it is therefore impossible for you really to judge their quality. But, if you see them first, remember that good oats are very hard, heavy, light in colour and comparatively rounded, dry-smelling and free from dust.

*Flaked maize* is a good fattening food. It has a high energy value but is low in protein, and so should not be used alone.

*Barley*, either flaked or boiled before feeding, also helps to put flesh on a horse. Do not use wheat.

*Sugar beet*, in the form of dry pulp or nuts, is also good for fattening and adding bulk, but is not a suitable feed for fast work. It must be soaked for at least twelve hours before feeding. It swells up, and it is absolutely essential that this phenomenon should occur outside your horse, unless you want him to burst.

*Linseed cake* is dear, but is useful in very small quantities, especially for horses in rather low condition and also to improve the coat. But do not try to experiment with preparing linseed yourself. Unless properly boiled first, it will poison your horse.

*Horse cubes* are a useful convenience food which can replace other concentrated feeds. They are very skilfully and scientifically compounded, and the mineral and vitamin additives may lead you to think that they and they only contain the secret of health and a long life. Do not be carried away by this. And check the labels carefully, because there is not much point in feeding a semi-idle cart gelding with a ration specially designed for a pregnant or suckling mare or for a racehorse in full training. There are no 'cart-horse cubes'. Your local supplier should be able to give you detailed counsel: but in general you will probably regard these branded feeds as a useful supplement and a standby in emergencies.

You may have read about peas and beans, but these are far too heating for the amateur to experiment with, especially on an animal that is working little. To have your horse on fire, prancing all over the place like a boxer demonstrating how he is shortly going to knock hell out of his opponent, may appear to be giving him a merry life. But it will be a short one, possibly for you as well as him. Some people say horses will eat silage. It would be idiotic to try whether yours will. The appalling damage that might result, if things went wrong, is best left to the imagination.

While bearing in mind our eighth principle, the avoidance of an abrupt and radical change of diet, do try to ring the changes between wet and dry foods. A horse will not be very happy with the monotony of eating dry stuff – hay, chaff and oats – every day during the winter.

In addition, since the prices of various feeds fluctuate considerably, you may be forced gradually to adjust the feeding from time to time on grounds of economy.

Provide just a little of something special sometimes, something to give him an interest in his food. A nice bit of chopped carrot or apple is very welcome. Or how about some mangold, if you can get any? Clean if off with a knife before slicing it. A stone inside a lump of mud might break a tooth. If you live near a brewery, some brewer's grains could be added from time to time. We all know that horses like beer, too, but do not give your horse a taste for this expensive refreshment, however much you love him.

How much food, how much of any constituent feeding stuffs, should you give your horse? You alone can discover the answer to that question, for it is your horse, not ours. We know neither its age, life-style or appetite, nor the season you are thinking about, nor what pasture you have, nor anything else about him or you. Your Trusty Adviser will come into his own here.

Victorian and Edwardian experts were rarely reluctant to fill page after page with dietary systems for heavy horses in hard work. They frequently contradicted each other, but most agreed that the heaviest horses (much heavier than yours today, unless you have the biggest in Britain) would consume up to 18lb of hay and 20lb of concentrated feed in a working day. If you gave your horse really hard work for nine hours a day, six days a week, he might need that: and if you gave it to him on the seventh day (that is, provided you were not already dead with exhaustion yourself), he would immediately get so ill that you would have to call the vet in a panic on Monday morning.

In contrast, one eminent authority spoke delightfully of the horse of 'the inferior farmer'. Often subsisting on hay or grass, the animal 'rarely gets a feed of corn, but maintains himself in tolerable condition, and does the work that is required of him: but this will not support a horse under hard work. Other substances containing a larger proportion of nutriment in a smaller compass, should be added.'

The feeding of farm stock has nowadays become a science because the objectives, clear and limited, can be precisely measured – weight gain, milk yield, and so on. The life of the horse, however, is different. It resembles ours, especially in two respects. The aim is physical fitness (not fatness) at all times, whether in leisure or work, idleness or activity; and longevity. His feeding, therefore, is not a science but an art.

The items of equipment you will need are a manger; feed bucket; dipper; scales (though you will soon find out how much your dipper holds); chaff-cutter; hay-rack; corn-bin; and clean water buckets.

A hay-rack is better than a net, which is difficult to fill, may become undone and possibly end up under your horse's feet instead of where it ought to be. Alternatively, he might get himself hung up in it. Keep the net for its proper purpose, as a portable and temporary hay-rack when you are out at a show.

The corn-bin should have a good lid, and perhaps a lock. If it is in the stable itself, it is essential that the horse cannot help himself to its contents, should he get free. Many a one has gorged himself to death that way. It must also be proof against vermin, which spoil more than they eat. The lock, if you need one, is not to keep vermin out.

A water bucket should not be left in with the horse. He will probably tread on it and both will suffer. If he is indoors all the time, it is best to take him out three or four times a day to drink. It saves you lugging water buckets around; it also gives him a chance to stretch his legs, and you an opportunity to see if he is moving all right and is not lame.

## Bedding

The quantity of material required for your horse to stand on comfortably indoors, or to lie on if he wishes, will obviously depend on whether he is in a stall or whether you have a whole loose box to carpet. And the proportion of it which will need renewing every morning is partly determined by this, because when he is stalled the dung is lying conveniently behind him, whereas it will be all over the place in a box. But it is also to some extent governed by the material you use.

With wheat or barley straw, your morning job is to push forward what is clean right up as far as you can and then to remove, with the dung, what is dirty. Then you sweep out and add as much fresh straw as necessary when re-making the bedding. The mixture of straw and dung will make good manure.

Peat moss can be used, but its disadvantages are expense and its tendency to stain the horse. On the other hand, the dung can be easily picked up from it and you remove only what you cannot help taking because it is stuck to the dung. The peat should be raked over in remaking the bed, and will need partial renewing from time to time. Like straw, it helps to make saleable manure.

On wood shavings, horses stay cleaner, and you will not have completely to renew the bedding more than perhaps two or three times a year, though of course you will have to add a little from time to time to replace the bits that are inadvertently removed with the dung. You can get a special prong which will leave almost all the shavings behind. This is particularly important because, mixed in the dung-heap, they make it largely useless. Shavings are no good for anything after they have finished their bedding career. You can only bury them.

One thing to watch, with shavings and peat, is that they block the drains if you are not careful, because they absorb moisture. You can overcome this by taking out the grating and putting a bag in. The drain must be outside the stable and all liquid should run right out freely and quickly.

Incidentally, horses which have been walking or standing for a long time on hard surfaces have an irritating propensity to urinate on nice clean bedding as soon as they enter their stall or box. (The very word *stale* derives from the same word as stall.) This is not a dirty habit – indeed, it is the reverse. They are fastidious creatures, most reluctant to splash themselves by staling on tarmac or stones. Consequently, they will wait a long time for the nearest equivalent to non-splash grass. To get annoyed about this is as sensible as objecting to the cat bringing mice into the house on autumn evenings or the dog removing a bone from his dinner table in order to gnaw it elsewhere. If you must stop your horse doing it after he has spent hours going up and down the High Street, stand him on the lawn for a few moments as soon as you are home, and see what happens. You may realise how much he has been looking forward to that moment.

Your manure heap should not be sited just outside the stable door; nor, for that matter, under the kitchen window. But you do not want it half a mile away. You will have no difficulty in selling your surplus good, clean cart-horse manure. There is none finer, and make certain that you charge the current price.

The implements you will need are a hay-prong with a short handle for clearing out – or a shavings-prong; brush; shovel; fork; stable-barrow (twice the size of an ordinary wheelbarrow); and hose-pipe. Avoid over-long handles on all equipment. They get in the way when you are manoeuvring in awkward places around horses.

## Grooming

In a horse's skin are billions of oil glands and sweat glands. These work with perfect efficiency in natural conditions, without any external maintenance. A horse moving around and feeding, and enjoying a little exercise when he pleases, has no trouble in ridding himself of the impurities created by the functions of his body. Even his dandruff is dispersed as fast as it is formed, by the natural elements of wind and rain.

It is when hard work has to be performed and sweating occurs, and when rich food is given to enable him to perform his duties, that exudations enormously increase. It has been estimated that a horse hard at work all day, and fed accordingly, excretes as much through his skin as he does through his bowels. Sometimes you can see him steaming, but mostly you do not notice anything at all, any more than you can see what comes off a wet towel on the clothes line. When the glands work overtime, they tend to become clogged and choked because their products are mixed with dry scurf, and this is made worse when actual sweat also dries.

Scurf is particles of dried skin. If you measure the quantity of 'dust' in a room that you occupy, and compare it with the lack of dust when the room has been empty, you will have some idea of the amount of powdered dead skin that we daily slough off. And, like horses but unlike some other animals, we are also sweaters. We need to unclog our pores. But we are not totally covered in hair. A horse's hair becomes dry, harsh and staring when the glands are choked. Worse still, beneath that surface the whole body is full of poisons and impurities that ought to have been eliminated, and the animal's health suffers as a consequence.

The true purpose of grooming, therefore, is to maintain health in an animal that we have chosen to use for our own purposes. There is an old saying that 'a good grooming is worth a feed of corn'. A pleasing appearance or a shining coat is, or should be, secondary. Of course this secondary reason is a perfectly valid one, but nothing should be done in trying to achieve it which would hamper or spoil the attainment of the primary object of fitness. That is why chemicals and other aids used by many horse owners in the past in order to achieve superficial beauty for show day do in fact eventually make the horse worse than before, for they interfere with his natural health.

An extra bonus achieved by grooming is that, if the skin is healthy, parasites will not lodge themselves in it so readily. And it helps to

Grooming kit, laid out on a stable rubber. At the top (from left to right) are a dandy brush, body brush, water brush and curry comb: below these, sponge, mane comb and hoof pick

discourage and disturb any that may already be there, with the exception of bot eggs (see Chapter 4, page 72).

There is one more principle to bear in mind. A horse sheds its coat twice each year, in spring and autumn. The hairs of the summer coat are shorter than those of the winter one. It is not an objective of grooming to hasten the removal of the old coat, so one should remember this when one has the brush in hand. It does no good to the animal at all if you leave him with bald patches.

How often, then, should you groom your horse, to keep him well?

Clearly, that is an impossible question to answer. It should be re-worded: *When* should you groom? This depends not on whether the horse is living in or out, as one might at first suppose, but on how hard he is working and what food he is receiving. If he is not working, and if he is living out in winter, he needs the grease in his coat to protect him. Although he may look scruffy, he is all right. But every time dried sweat binds dust and dirt and scurf and grease into solid little masses, he will require grooming.

If the horse is soaked with sweat, leave the harness on for a while, unless you can attend to him immediately. It will not do for him suddenly to have all his 'clothes' off and to stand naked. The sweat will evaporate too quickly and chill him. If it is only rain on him, that will not matter much. As soon as you can, however, take the harness off and immediately wipe him down with a wisp. This is hay twisted into a sort of rope, but if you have not learned how to make one, use just a handful of hay, or straw.

Now to grooming. Yesterday's dried sweat has to come off before he can work today. If there is caked mud and moulting hair as well, begin with the dandy brush, but not on sensitive parts of the coat such as the inside of the thighs. (If you want to know why, try its long and tough and widely spaced bristles on yourself.) His face is not likely to be encrusted with dirt but if it is, he will not be happy if you take a dandy brush to it. Exert only the minimum vigour to do the job, and shake the brush clean after each short stroke that you make.

You are now ready to work hard. Put your hand through the strap of the body brush and take the curry comb in the other hand. Beginning at the head and working steadily back down one side of the horse, use long strokes of the brush, following the direction of the hairs. Do not just smooth or tickle him. Press hard, and not merely with the strength of your arm. Stand far enough back to be able to put your full weight behind your efforts. After each stroke, clean the brush by drawing it across the curry comb and, as often as necessary, tap the comb on the floor to empty it of what has come off the horse.

Now go down the other side, beginning with the head again and turning the mane over as necessary. Now consider him. Have you finished? Make certain you have not omitted the top of his back, or the other parts that you cannot easily reach. Have you forgotten up between the legs? Or the base of the ears? And if you want to make your horse glow with health, and you can learn to make a hay-wisp, give his neck and body and the tops of his legs a vigorous massage with that, using short firm strokes in the direction of the hairs.

Take a damp sponge or piece of towelling and wipe his nose and round his eyes. Take another one, and sponge underneath his tail.

Use a metal comb on his mane and tail, going carefully and patiently so that eventually all tangles and obstructions are cleared, and you can put the comb right in and draw it easily to the very end of the hairs. Have you childish memories of your hair being combed? Some of us found it soothing, even sensual. Less fortunate children were attacked as if by someone raking stones out of long grass.

A thick tail is not good, and some get very thick. It is liable to become so tangled with knots and clits and lumps of muck that its owner is scarcely able to swish it at all. This is almost as useless as, and more uncomfortable than, having no tail at all. There is a way of 'pulling' the tail and the mane, and, in hairy-legged types of horse, the feather as well, to improve the utility as well as the beauty of these hirsute parts. It is done by twisting one or two unwanted hairs at a time over the back of the mane comb and then sharply jerking. But you should get an experienced person to show you how to do this. It does not hurt if you do it properly, but is not enjoyed by the horse if performed clumsily, reviving the rake-in-the-grass syndrome, or if too much is done in one session.

You may have the bright idea of buying an electric groomer. Some of these are very good indeed: others are less so. If you have only one horse you will regard it as absurdly expensive, unless you have very little time, a weak back or flabby arms. In any case, you will probably regard this work as your social half-hour with the horse, and will want to give him personal attention and to experience the satisfaction of close physical contact, rather than rush the job through mechanically. Horses, mostly, like being groomed and so will yours, if you do it properly. But if you end up with six horses and no one to help you, you will change your mind about electric groomers.

Pick up each foot and look at it. How to do this without an unseemly struggle, and why, and what you might have to do before putting it down again, are explained in Chapter 4 (page 82).

In winter, if your horse does a lot of heavy work it might be a good idea to trace-clip him. On the face of it, this might seem a crazy idea. Surely the reason nature provides horses with a winter coat is that they need to keep warm? Indeed they do, and to clip yours would certainly be crazy if he were to do only the lightest of work, or none at all, and stay out of doors for much of the day. But the horse which earns his keep by regular hard work and is wearing a thick heavy coat is unable to sweat as he should. He becomes far too hot in the cold

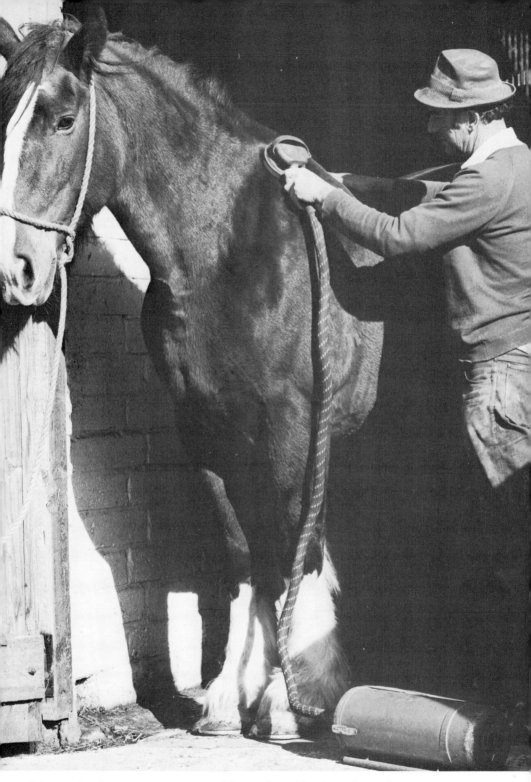

Using an electric groomer: on some models a variety of heads can be used

air, cannot lose the heat, becomes quickly exhausted, and the glands in his skin become quickly clogged. Nature did not create the species for hard draught or for being ridden fast in the hunting field: and so unnatural activity requires an unnatural remedy. Only you can make a decision and this will probably be difficult, because your horse's winter routine will lie half-way between real work and real holiday.

Trace-clipping is a partial hair-cut, of the lower part of his body and the tops of his legs – the area between two horizontal lines, one running from the point of his shoulder to the back of the thigh and the other from half-way down the forearm back to his lower thigh. This enables him to sweat sufficiently, but still leaves protection against cold rain on top and mud on the legs. It is best done before the winter coat is fully grown, say in October, and will probably have to be repeated at least once.

It is not worth buying an electric clipper for one horse and so, if you want it done, get someone to do it for you. Should you want to have a go yourself, remember to use the clipper against the lie of the hair, as barbers used to do in the short-back-and-sides era.

It is pleasant to turn to a summer topic. Grooming for show is an art. Some people can make an old clothes-horse into an eye-catcher, especially if they have a hairy sort to work on. In the very old days, when Shires were really shaggy, one famous exhibitor used to say 'Give me some hair, and I can make a horse'. No one can become such an artist overnight, and we shall have to content ourselves with principles.

Operating by hand, you should begin weeks before the season starts, and groom twice a day. The occasional use of an electric groomer is a great help at this time, if you can borrow one. You want your horse shining and you will have to work hard at it. You can get the dust off and polish a summer coat beautifully glossy with a dry stable rubber – but only if the skin is healthy and the friction of good grooming has stimulated the oil glands.

Two special words for you if your horse is grey – bad luck. Grass and dung stains show up remarkably well on a grey coat. As you cannot dye him brown, you will have to get the stains out, which means a shampoo all over. This is all right in summer, but in cold weather the horse will not like it any more than you do. And he may easily catch cold unless you dry him promptly and properly. You must use something which is kind to your hands – and therefore to his skin; not a strong detergent. Soft soap is required, or a proprietary brand of animal shampoo.

Legs, particularly white ones, must be washed. You need warm water, and more of your soft soap. Rinse off with more warm water to make sure you have got all the soap out. (By the way, wash the black ones as well as the white.) It is vital to dry them properly to avoid the risk of cracked or greasy heels and, if your horse is the hairy-legged Shire type, this is quite a business. A lot of the water will be flicked out if you trot the horse twenty yards and back again on a clean dry surface.

Now you need some wood flour – ground-up white sawdust, from a sanding machine. On no account use any coloured wood flour, it *must* be white. If you cannot obtain it (and there are not many places where you can), it is possible, though not so effective, to use ordinary sawdust as long as it is white and dry.

Stand one of the fore-feet on a split-open bag or something large enough to catch all the spare flour. Rub the flour really well into the first leg until it is completely dry. Now do the other three legs in turn. All the wood flour that has fallen on to the bag can be gathered up for another time. What you have rubbed in will gradually fall out again. In your final preparation before entering the ring, you can brush any remaining flour out with a dandy brush before doing the feather with a mane comb.

If you are simply wishing to present your horse in 'decent' rather than show condition, say with a view to sale, a bucket of warm water with an eggcupful of household paraffin in it will take all the muck and grease out quite quickly. Put it on with a water brush, and use your fingers to get it right in.

The following items comprise your grooming kit: water brush; dandy brush; body brush; curry comb; stable rubbers; mane comb; sponges or cloths; (electric groomer); (clipper); bucket; soft soap; wood flour; hoof pick and hoof oil (see Chapter 4) – and a bag to keep brushes, combs etc in. Nothing is more irritating than to mislay an item of grooming kit. In any case, if you go to shows you will have to take everything with you. Do not forget to have face and dock sponges boiled clean after each use and to maintain everything, like your own toiletries, in immaculate condition.

# 4

# Healthy Mind and Healthy Body

Proper feeding, watering, bedding and grooming are one part of what is necessary for your horse's welfare. The other is outlined here – the maintenance of mental health (placed first not without reason), general physical fitness, and the soundness of his limbs, as far and as long as you are able. When you fail (and this need never be your fault if you use common sense), it is time to call for veterinary help. If you believe we should have said more about various maladies, you are wrong. And you are more wrong if you think we ought to have told you how to cure them. Mr Pope remarked, as long ago as 1711, that 'a little learning is a dang'rous thing'. It is never more dangerous than when applied to sickness, human or animal.

### Personal relations

Since the horse is by nature a herd animal, a mare or gelding readily accepts a servant–master relationship with humans, if this is sympathetically established. We hope, therefore, that your acquisition has been expertly 'broken'. This word is almost a technical term but is most inapt. Learning discipline and learning to work should never break a horse's spirit and are not cruel, provided that the lessons are given with understanding and at the right time (see Chapter 7).

We hope also that he has been correctly treated by his previous owners. Provided that this is so, in spite of his enormous size and strength, you will have little trouble with him – if you, in your turn, appreciate what the relationship should be. If not, you will have no difficulty in completely spoiling him. A stallion, however impeccable his previous record, would give the beginner plenty of trouble, for he has the instinctive ambition to attain independence for himself and mastery over others. That is one of the reasons why you will not be buying a stallion. A lion would be safer, as long as you kept giving him strong meat: rich food fed to a stallion would make him worse than ever.

You most show only two emotions towards your horse. The first is love – the love of the creator for the created (he will make you his god), a love which has nothing to do with any attractive attributes of the beloved. The second is pleasure at what he does well and, conversely, displeasure when he does wrong. In the way you express these feelings, you must be absolutely unvarying; not unpredictable, peevish, impatient, excitable, hard or soft, or hot or cold.

Your horse, on the other hand, is liable to display any emotions that he might feel at any particular moment. These may be intensified by illness or some other physical discomfiture. At times, he may have nasty memories of something that happened when he belonged to someone else. You must discover and understand his problems.

Like any servant, he will occasionally 'try it on'. Then you must give him a sharp token of your displeasure, so that he does not do it again. If his idea of a joke is to nip the seat of your pants when you are bending down, it is up to you to decide whether you share the mirth. He might carry it too far and, although perhaps acceptable to you, the same joke played on others would not be amusing.

The more intelligent he is, the more likely he is to 'play up' – and the better he will be at his work. Everyone would prefer an intelligent horse to a dullard. Two horses might both be intelligent, but in different ways. A third may be clever only when he feels like it.

Breed makes no difference. The Suffolk, Shire, Clydesdale and Percheron display the same range of equine brain-power. Nor does sex, or its absence, affect the issue. To claim that stallions are more intelligent than geldings must be absurd. An animal's IQ cannot be reduced by removing its testicles. Castration abates the swiftness of his responses, and his fiery determination to translate into action what occurs to his mind – but that is all. Years ago, work-horses used often to be dulled by overwork and exhaustion. Nowadays the same effect is more likely to be produced by prolonged idleness and loneliness, with nothing to occupy either their talents or their hearts.

Equine intelligence has long been debated, and the horse's exceptional powers of memory of course confuse the arguments. But, in practice, where is the difference? The furrow horse who understands where he must put his feet when ploughing; the milk horse who knows which houses contain his customers and which do not; the pair of horses abreast which have learnt, when turning to left or right, how much slower or faster to move so as to keep level with each other –

scores of examples could be quoted of sufficient teachability for any task a man could require of a non-human assistant. But if you start with the premise that you are dealing with a dumb and stupid creature, and treat him so, you will find that you have made him just what you thought.

You are never going to get anywhere unless you teach him discipline, set him a standard, encourage him, praise him when he deserves it and communicate with him. He is in these respects like a child. If you examine the behaviour of the teenager, you can discern how many of these advantages he has had in childhood. So let us now consider communication, which between man and horse is achieved through the three senses of touch, sound and sight. We can forget smell and taste, for these are receptive rather than communicatory.

Touch is the most primitive of the senses. When you go to your horse, or when he comes to you, touch him. Stroke his face. Pat him. It is mainly on the head and neck that touch communicates your love for him. But get him used to being touched at any point of his anatomy, because at some time or another you will have to do so.

Touch can also communicate your displeasure. Physical punishment may be the only way of teaching him that he must not repeat what he has just done. It must be immediate – half a minute later is no good. If he tries to bite you, he should receive a smart smack on the chops. Even if he does not learn the first time, he will soon realise that the consequence is as certain as the shock from an electric fence. Five little taps are no use. At the fourth, he may wonder what game you are playing, and bite two of your fingers off.

To be corrective and therefore constructive, punishment must be sufficient, but no more than sufficient. If to growl at him is enough, then just growl at him. Use the minimum force, if any is needed. For example, if he is obviously considering whether to kick, a smack on the buttocks with a cupped hand can make a noise which is tremendous compared with the very slight pain it causes. But it would make any reasonably minded horse reconsider the matter, which is what you desire. On the other hand, there may be times when several good whacks with a stout stick are required. Punishment must be over once it is administered. If you appear on crutches because he has cracked your shin, or with your arm bound up because he has bitten it, he will not associate the crutches or the bandage with his own misdemeanour. Nor will he feel remorse, which is a purely human emotion.

Your horse, in his turn, will communicate with you by touch also – for example, by pushing his head against your chest. To communicate petulance or anger, he is singularly well equipped, being able to bite; to strike forwards very dangerously with a foreleg; to kick with a hind leg backwards, and very sharply with a hind leg suddenly brought forwards. Being no fool, he can express real hatred simply by getting you against a wall and then leaning his weight on you with the simple aim of crushing your ribs.

A horse standing on three legs cannot kick. He has to be on all four. If he is, and you put your hand on the top of his rump, forward of the tail, you will feel a muscle twitch when he is going to kick. When grooming your horse, rest a hand on his back to detect that warning. Also he has to bring the leg forward a little way first – another sign. If you do get caught, remember that the closer you are the less your injury will be. A strike with a foreleg is, unfortunately, almost impossible to anticipate. Even if your horse 'never kicks', do not do anything silly, such as snoozing in a deckchair just behind him. A quiet one may kick unexpectedly – not at you, but it would prove just as painful whatever the intention.

In interpreting a horse's less pleasing physical contacts, you have to decide whether they are due to accident, not knowing his own strength, silliness, irritability caused by some sort of pain or tenderness, or hatred. The latter you are unlikely to encounter, unless you have a mature stallion which is plotting to get his own back against you (your fault) or a previous owner (bad luck on you), or is one of the wicked ones.

Most actions which might lead to your being hurt should be foreseen – and will be, when you have experience. Do not turn your horse round in his box if you cannot get out of the way and must be pushed against the wall. If you know he is ticklish in a certain spot, then be careful what you do. And so on – common sense really.

Oral communication with your horse should begin with your giving him a name that he can instantly recognise. A two-syllable name is best, or one that can be pronounced as two syllables. That is why such names as Captain, Colonel, Major or Vi-let and Di-mon' have always been popular. Each is entirely different from any other, and is not too long. Do not be tempted to shorten it to one syllable. He must know you are speaking to him and not to another.

For vital commands, find out what your new horse's vocabulary is. The words vary in different parts of Britain. If he comes from Scotland, he may not at first understand your Somerset talk. You must make allowances while he is re-learning.

Occasionally, a horse will think he hears a command, act upon it

– and be mistaken. On one occasion a man was loading muck into a cart. He had twice been told it was dinner time, so his wife appeared to shout 'come on' at him. But it was the horse that came on, not him. It was no good getting cross with the horse.

Apart from using his name and the few precise instructions that he must learn, it does not really matter what you say to your horse, as long as you say something – except when he is working, as we mention later. Like other animals, he likes being talked to, but it is only the intonation of your voice that he understands. This will convey your pleasure at seeing him: and, when necessary, it will also communicate your displeasure.

It is especially important to give him an advance greeting when for any reason he might not otherwise know you are there. If you creep up behind him in your bedroom slippers when he is half asleep in his stall at the dead of night, do not blame him if he kicks you into the intensive care unit.

In general, the quieter and the more soothing your voice, the better. True horsemen tend to be soft spoken, just as they are calm and unflurried movers. Occasionally, it may be necessary to bawl your horse out, and the surprise will be salutary. On the other hand, he may be an animal which only gets nervous if you shout at him. With four horses, you might roar at one, but succeed only in upsetting the other three.

Try, for your part, to learn to interpret horse-sounds, although with a couple of geldings you will never hear the full equine range of whicker, whinny and neigh; squeal, snort, sigh; groan, grunt, roar and trumpet. These express the emotions of foal, mare and stallion in the course of their lives – pleasure, greeting; surprise or fear; anger; exertion; lust; and so on. In addition, there are the enquiring sounds, the where-are-you and the who's-there, an infinite variety such as you would make if you had the voice-box of *Equus caballus* and if the discipline of early training had not conditioned you to a constant attempt to disguise rather than express your emotions. The only non-verbal sound accepted in polite society is the laugh, which expresses the one emotion absent from the horse's experience, even though we loosely called the nip-in-the-pants a joke.

Visual communication is particularly important, but only in one direction – from him to you. If you twitch your ears, he will not be impressed, because they are poor things and in the wrong place. (One expert, however, has discovered that by extending three fingers of each hand above the top of his head and moving them about, he can obtain a most gratifying reaction from most horses.) Nor can a horse see the difference between smiling and scowling. He notices only startlingly unfamiliar things – and does not like them. If you appeared before him in a paper hat or with an open umbrella, he would not understand you to be filled with a festive spirit or afraid of getting wet, but he would be suspicious. Should you lie on the ground before him, he would be very inquisitive, but incapable of divining that you were tired or contemplating the beauties of nature.

On the other hand, a horse has a sixth sense, non-visual, which is very perceptive. He knows when we are frightened of him, however much we may try to disguise the fact. He has a special insight into inebriation, too. In the old days, many a stallion leader, trudging with his charge from farm to pub and pub to farm sixty or seventy miles a week, and finding himself in pedestrian difficulties, would put his hand through the horse's girth. The leader would be led. Or if the infirmity grew worse, and the man fell down, the horse would stand protectively with him for hours until the weakness had passed, instead of wreaking havoc in the neighbourhood as he would normally do when not under the strictest control.

At other times a horse may appear, to us, quite silly. In the days when grooms had to use a lantern on dark mornings, they had to be especially careful to greet their horses audibly, so that the animals turned to face them. If the horse was the other way about, he would be terrified by his own vast shadow thrown on the wall. This was not because he was feeble-minded but because a horse's eyesight is different from ours.

In communicating visually with other horses, and therefore also with you, his ears are particularly expressive. They can range from the forward pricked position, showing that he is curious or vigilant, to being laid back practically flat against his head to denote that he is about to commit murder. It would be confusing, if not impossible, to attempt a glossary of ear positions. In any case, it is much more instructive to observe your own horse and get into the habit of trying to guess what he is thinking. It is the only way of learning. Although the primary function of the ears is to act as receivers, the fact that the horse is able to adjust them to the direction whence the sound waves are coming can also act as an extra guide to what is in his mind.

The various movements of the muscles controlling the nose and the lips and mouth are also revealing to other horses. They will be more difficult for you to interpret, but an equally rewarding task.

The eyes, much as the horse may vary the position of their lids in pain or pleasure, communicate comparatively little to other members of his species. To you, they will reveal chiefly his physical condition and general temperament rather than his random thoughts or passing moods. If you can discern, from the way he looks at you, that he wants something, you are making progress. If you can sense that it is a drink he wants, you are understanding him well.

When perhaps you buy another horse you will have to learn to know him, too. He will be a stranger at first. Remember, also, that your new horse may not get on very well with the first one. Or they may become great friends. It is not just you and the horses, but you and two others – three personalities. One horse may not like working with another, but get on famously with a third.

You must spend time with your horse. Visit him daily anyway, even if he is living out, even a couple of miles away. Look him over carefully. That is the time to stop for a chat, three times on a Sunday if you like. But there is no virtue in that if you do not go to him on Monday and Tuesday.

A certain dyspeptic employer was irritated by the hearty way in which one of his staff greeted him each morning. Normally he just grunted, but one day he said 'Good morning, good morning, good morning. That'll do for three mornings.' You cannot adopt that attitude with your horse. It is a form of cruelty against which he is defenceless. Because he is not particularly demonstrative, he will patiently stand around in his paddock for days without a single person, human or equine, as company. If yours has to do that, do him a good turn – get rid of him to someone better fitted to own a horse.

Finally, remember not only that he has a personality of his own deserving respect, but that it is a *horse* personality. He has a *horse* mind. To say that an animal is 'almost human' is to reveal one's own folly. An almost-human horse would not be a proper horse. Nevertheless, it is not really contradictory to say that you should treat a horse like a child. A child is potentially 'naughty'. With a naughty child you must be firm – and kind. A child can tell if you dislike him, and if you are weak. So can a horse. In either of these situations, neither your child nor your horse will be happy and well behaved.

## Health and sickness

A wise man will discreetly enquire from other horse-owners about vets before he buys his horse. There are of course good and bad vets, but lazy or careless ones are doubtless rarer than negligent doctors because there is no national animal health service and their income derives wholly from their clients who get what they pay for and (we hope) pay for what they get.

Vets are remarkable men and women, competent with canaries, cats or cattle and ready on request to examine a bear or baboon. Furthermore, unlike doctors, they do not refer the trickier medical cases and all the surgical ones to specialists. They do it all themselves, specialising only in so far as the location, size and organisation of their practice allow them. If you live in a farming district, big-animal vets will be more plentiful than in the middle of Birmingham or Bradford. You will be especially lucky in a horsy area, for there will be vets whose happiness is measured by the proportion of equine patients they have. The man who has examined thousands of horses will handle yours more expertly, diagnose the trouble more infallibly and effect a cure more quickly. If the malady is rare, he will have met it once before or has been dreaming of the day when he will come across it for the first time. Mr Lamb, Mr Pidgeon or even Mr Bull might justifiably propose to shoot your horse. Mr Horseman might cure him.

Your first meeting with Mr H can be when you ask him to come to have a look at your new horse and, specifically, to propose a worming programme for him. Horses have worms – specialised ones whose very lives depend solely upon horses or asses or zebras. Whatever you do, your horse will have worms, but you must see to it that he does not have too many. If it were not for these, you would have nothing unpleasant to think about, for horses are so designed that in all their parts they are clean and wholesome. Even their dung is tidy and neatly packaged.

The strongyles comprise more than half the forty or more kinds of horse-worms. Strong and tough, they may be up to two inches long, and the most dastardly are the common or red ones. They are not really red, but look it when full of blood which they suck as they hang on the gut. They spend part of their early lives actually in the blood vessels, and this is not nice, either, because they can cause anaemia, perhaps not surprising in view of their inordinate greed. They are the most frequent cause of colic.

Fatal colic, causing rupture of the gut, can also be brought about by roundworms, another loathsome enemy. As thick as a pencil and up to nearly a foot long, they can muster in numbers sufficient to completely block the bowel of a young horse. They also lay millions of eggs, which are hard and sticky and able to survive for ages in the stable or on grass, waiting for an unsuspecting horse to swallow them. These worms, too, lead interesting lives, for when young they spend a period of time in the lung.

In contrast, the curious tapeworms, measuring up to three inches, are relatively harmless. They are sometimes passed out in the dung. This is not attractive to observe, though less astonishing than an occasional roundworm or cluster of red ones. However, the sight of a complete worm will give you little clue to the number that you never see. If an ounce of dung contains less than about three thousand eggs in late summer, you and your horse are doing well. If there are ten times as many, your management is poor. Fortunately, not every egg becomes a worm.

Pin or seat worms favour the colon and rectum and lay eggs round the anal ring. This odious habit irritates the horse and he rubs his rump so much that he is likely to wear the hair off his tail. Lung-worms prefer donkeys, but when they find themselves inside a horse, retaliate by causing him more trouble than their preferred hosts. A sound reason for not keeping an ass, quite apart from the cacophony of his oral communications.

What shall we say of threadworms, which can live anywhere – in tendons, skin and even the eyes? Nothing. Let us ignore also all the non-worm parasites, such as ticks and lice and give dishonourable mention to only two or three flies.

The common horse-fly is the light brown one that picks you out with her beautiful eyes (they really are) and in stealthy silence lands on your flesh while you are mowing the lawn in late summer, to drive her dagger-like jaws into you. Absorbed in her vampire's work, she ceases to be alert and you can murder her with a quick smack, unless she gets you between the shoulder-blades. But she is a petty foe, using humans and horses only as a dinner-plate. She lays her eggs on leaves. The dilettante male does not even bite, but spends his time hovering in sylvan glades, sipping nectar and drinking from cool streams.

The bot-fly neither feeds nor drinks. She has no mouth, but is nastier altogether. During her brief life of total abstinence, she deposits her eggs on the horse's skin. When these hatch, the horse nibbles himself and swallows the grubs, which are pleased about this because they can stay all winter long in his stomach. Not for nothing are they called Gasterophiles. Later, they pass out of the body and, within about three weeks, become flies, thus beginning the whole grisly cycle again. Bots may seem small fry, but they often perforate the gut and can cause peritonitis and very severe colic. Unfortunately, when still on the horse's outer skin, the grubs benefit from grooming which seems to stimulate them to grow. The only way to remove them is with a warm wet sponge or a special scraper called a bot-knife.

The bot's wretched cousin, the warble, is supposed to lay her eggs on cattle, but occasionally chooses a horse. The maggots penetrate the skin and wander round beneath it for months, causing horrid swellings as they grow and, when about an inch long, prepare to pop out. Fortunately, warbles have no friends among conservationists and have been dealt hefty blows by modern man.

Let us return to our worms. If your horse has too many, the skin becomes dry and tight, the dung loose, and in extreme cases the belly protuberant – which is scarcely surprising, since the liver, lungs and blood vessels are affected as well as the stomach and intestines. There are three ways in which to deal with these pests.

Firstly, get your vet to prescribe a comprehensive worm paste, not to smear on your horse, but for him to eat. Use the full recommended dose (a cart-horse has a big worm area), and no less often than instructed. But the enemy is crafty, and will find ways of coping with your onslaughts, so keep him on his toes by getting the ammunition changed every fourth or fifth treatment. Ruthless bombardment will make most of the worms turn their toes up. The height of the battle will be in July and August, but you must keep up the cannonade. The worm-slayer can also incorporate a bot-destroyer in the autumn.

Secondly, regular rotation of grazing in your paddocks will do much to encourage tiny worms hatched from dung to die while vainly waiting for a horse to eat them. If consumed by cattle, they accept the mistake, and expire immediately. So the rotation, giving each paddock three weeks' rest in four from horse grazing, together with any harrowing or mowing you may do in warm weather and the cropping by your neighbour's cattle, will get plenty of sun and air to the little worms which, used to a dark environment, will perish. You cannot do anything else to kill the worms in pasture. Something to slay those tough roundworm eggs would obliterate the herbage as well.

Thirdly, nothing will help much if you allow someone else's wormy horse to share your paddocks. In negotiating with Miss Amanda Smith-Jones to let her keep her horse with yours in exchange for light holiday duties, tactfully introduce the subject of worms into the conversation. And if you buy a new horse, worm it and, if you can, isolate it for the first three days.

\*    \*    \*

Worms and flies apart, what can turn a fit horse into a sick one? The textbooks speak of a thousand and one things, many of them analogous to human disorders. Do not let these prey on your mind. Fearing, as we have already said, to lead the beginner into the danger of possessing a little learning, we shall speak only of colds, coughs, colic, and wounds. But, before that, let us list four infallible signs of real illness to which you should be alert.

The first is loss of appetite. If your horse will not eat, there is something wrong with him – unless there is something wrong with his food. Make sure it is not mouldy or otherwise unpalatable. Then look for other symptoms before being too prompt to ring the vet.

The second is his general appearance and demeanour. If he is listless, if his eyes are dull, if his ears are cold, if he hangs his head, if his coat is staring, there is something wrong with him. In winter of course his coat will be ragged and scruffy, but that is not what is meant. His skin is healthy if your fingers can freely slide it over the underlying flesh and muscle, especially at the neck and ribs. If it seems 'stuck' to them, it is not in good condition.

The third is his dung and urine. If there is anything really unusual about either of these – for example, an unpleasant smell from the former or a very dark brown colour in the latter – then you may need the vet. But do not worry about minor variations. The dung of a horse out at pasture will have a greenish look about it when first dropped. The urine of a healthy horse, sometimes almost colourless, may be on other occasions a dark yellow-brown and leave a noticeable deposit of solids. Failure to defecate or to stale at all is of course very serious, but then there will be additional signs of malaise, so there is no need to follow your horse around with a clock in case his bowels or bladder stop working.

And, fourth, there is his temperature. If you can read an ordinary clinical thermometer, smear it with vaseline and push it right into his anus, remembering of course to leave enough to get it out again; and it is wise not to stand directly behind him. The thermometer should read just over 100°F (38°C). It is a good idea to do this several times with a new horse when he is well, so that you know what his temperature normally is. In a few animals, it is always very slightly lower than this, or it drops slightly in the evening. Otherwise it will vary very little or not at all. If, therefore, you find it is 104°F (40°C), rush to the telephone.

Describe the symptoms as accurately as you can, including if possible the temperature. Should the horse keep shaking his head, there might be something very seriously wrong with his brain and he is about to go berserk: on the other hand, he might have something stuck in his teeth. If, however, you say that he has a temperature of 104° and a staring coat, will not eat, and is coughing and breathing fast, the vet will expect to find a case of pneumonia when he arrives. But do not tell him the horse *has* got pneumonia. And do not use the knowledge you have gleaned from textbooks to announce that you have a case of peritonitis, nephritis, or *purpura haemorrhagica*. Even if you are right, he will prefer to be the one to make the pronouncement.

However ignorant you are, the vet will not treat you as a fool, unless he gradually discovers that you are. It costs fools and ignorant folk more to keep a horse in good health, but the latter learn when to call the vet and when to wait a while. At first, the most intelligent owner will be genuinely worried that if he does not call the vet tonight, it will be the knacker-man in the morning.

A Trusty Adviser might be invaluable here. Even if you have to mollify him with largesse for calling him up just as he was going to bed, it will add to your peace of mind while waiting for the professional man to call.

When the vet does come, have your horse where he can do something with it. What can he do in the rain in the middle of a big field at night, with no hot water and only a torch? And do not do anything to confuse him. Do not coat your animal with tar or pour diesel oil all over him because some fool has advised you to do so. But if the vet gives you an instruction on the phone you should of course follow it.

Do whatever the vet tells you. Are you prepared to stick a needle into your horse? If the vet says he needs an injection twice a day for four days, it will cost you a lot of money if he has to come and do it himself.

Now to the colds, coughs and colic. If your horse catches a cold, he will get over it, like you do. He might have a bit of a cough with it. Give him a rest and look after him. He might also cough because he has something in his throat, or just wants to clear out his air passages, and he might then snort afterwards. But if he begins to cough often and it does not clear up with the cold, it might be that he is broken-winded, or that it is those lung-worms, or that he has *The Cough*. This is a virus infection, serious and catching. For the sake of other horses, he will need isolating. If he becomes hot or excited, he might drop dead. If he has a high temperature as well and is off his feed, he might have influenza or pneumonia. More work for the vet.

The horse is a finicky and selective feeder, and will not normally eat anything that is not good and wholesome, or anything he does not like. The ability of his lips and teeth to leave neatly behind the minutest thing that he does not want, whether in field or manger, and to eat everything else round it, is marvellous.

However, the most vulnerable part of his anatomical make-up is his digestive system. He can cope in any one hour with only a small portion of his total daily food intake. Furthermore, he is denied two of the reliefs useful to some other creatures – he can neither belch nor vomit. All his waste products have to leave his body via his bowels or his kidneys and bladder or his sweat-glands. These glands are very active, for his urine output in no way measures up to the water he drinks. His dung production is most impressive – perhaps more than a third of a hundredweight each day.

The wind he expels is often prodigious. But the time for you to worry is when he cannot expel it. Indigestion can result in an inability to release these gases, even though they are distending the stomach and intestines like balloons. This condition is colic. The bowels, stretched too wide, are unable to push their contents along. If the horse tries to urinate the pain is increased, so he stops trying. To relieve the agony, he may adopt all sorts of odd and grotesque postures. But the most dangerous thing he can do is to lie down and roll. He thinks it will help, but, with his internal organs in their present condition, he might twist his intestines or telescope part of them, either of which will completely block the bowel. Or he might develop a strangulated hernia. He might even rupture his stomach or intestines.

In all cases of colic, the beginner should call the vet at once and meanwhile try to keep the animal from lying down. Talk to him and encourage him to move about, if he can. If he does throw himself to the ground, keep him warm and put as much straw under and round him as you can, to prevent him from injuring himself as he twists his head and legs about.

You can cause colic by giving your horse a big drink after he has eaten a considerable quantity of concentrated food, by allowing him a lot of cold water when he is very hot, by offering him too much rich or unsuitable food, or by suddenly and radically changing his diet. Another cause of colic – and a serious one, as you cannot fail to remember – is worms. In fact, the commonest real horse-emergency is colic, and fatal colic is generally due to worms. Or bots.

Let us end with wounds. These should be cleaned with Dettol

diluted in warm water. There is also available a proprietary powder for small cuts. In the case of a bad wound, send for the vet. If stitching is required, the sooner the better. You may think it is impossible to stop the bleeding, but you can at least try to plug the hole. One man saved his horse's life by ramming handfuls of flour – the only suitable material to hand – into a wide and deep wound. This eventually coagulated the blood into a messy cake which oozed rather than poured blood. The vet, on arrival, scarcely warmed to the sight that met his eyes, but his patient was at least alive. There are times when you have to do something yourself, and at once.

One injury your horse should *never* have is harness galls. Nor will he, if the harness is kept in good condition and fits him properly. But the skin of a young horse is tender and in the event of galls the shoulders should be bathed in salt water. If the galls are very bad, you will have to get advice from the vet.

In your medicine cabinet you should keep a supply of Dettol, iodine, bandages, wound dressings, cotton wool, powder for cuts, worm paste and fly spray. Always dispose of the left-overs of any drug prescribed for a specific trouble.

## Leg, foot and shoe

'No foot, no horse' was the old saying, and nothing has ever made it out of date. A horse is no better than his feet and no better than his legs. The fitness of his legs depends more often than not on whether his feet are all right.

You may be only dimly aware of what happens after you stuff food down your throat. You may live a good life in ignorance of where your occipital bone is, or even that you have one. You may have no idea that your horse has one, too. But you must know something about his feet.

The horse walks, as everyone knows, on two fingernails at the front and two toenails at the back, forming his four hooves, since each fore-leg has only one finger and each hind-leg only one toe. We call these single toes his feet.

In the fore-leg, his shoulder-blade and his upper arm or humerus are within his body. The first part of the limb that you see separately is his elbow joint. Below that, his forearm is, unlike ours, fused into one bone instead of two, which is why he cannot turn his front hooves upside down to look at the bottom of them. The joint below his forearm ought, on the human analogy, to be called his wrist, but is

77

called his knee instead, which is confusing. The long bone leading to your middle finger, the one enclosed in your palm, is your horse's cannon bone.

Attached by a ligament to the cannon bone, one on each side, are the vestigial remains of two other fingers. These are the splint bones. At the bottom of the cannon bone, there are also two other little bones which have no corresponding equivalent in man. They are to help the tendons with the leverage of that part of the leg. At this fetlock joint begin the horse equivalents of the three free bones of your finger – the first and second pastern bones and the coffin or pedal bone, the latter being a little one entirely enclosed within the hoof. At the joint of the last two is another extra little bone, the navicular bone, to assist the leverage.

The hind limb of your horse corresponds, and with similar differences, to your leg. His femur, unlike your thigh, is enclosed in his body, and the first part of the leg you can feel from outside is the front of what in the human is the knee-cap and in the horse is called the stifle. His hock is therefore, anatomically speaking, equivalent to your ankle (which is very confusing indeed, for when we talk of a horse's ankles we mean something lower down the leg). Below the hock, the cannon bone, two pastern bones and so on are more or less as they are in the fore-leg.

More things go wrong with a horse's legs, and do so more often, than bear thinking about. This is not surprising when one reflects that, so far from leaving him to 'do his own thing', we ask some horses to run their fastest or run and jump with a human on their back and others to pull a load, very often on man-made unyielding surfaces.

Leg ailments can affect the *tendons*, particularly behind the cannon bone of the foreleg; the *ligaments*, causing curb at the back of the hock; the *joints*, producing arthritis, or stresses or bony growths such as bone spavin on the hock, or flabby swellings such as bog spavin; the *cartilages*, for example in the foot where its ossification results in sidebone; or the *bones* themselves, resulting in splint (a bony growth on the side of the cannon bone between itself and one of the splint bones) or ringbone (a bony deposit somewhere on one of the pastern bones) or navicular disease.

All these things, and more, can occur – just one of them can cripple him. Some of these conditions are hereditary – or, to be more accurate, a predisposition to them is hereditary. It is no wonder that a veterinary inspection is desired by anyone wanting to buy a really expensive

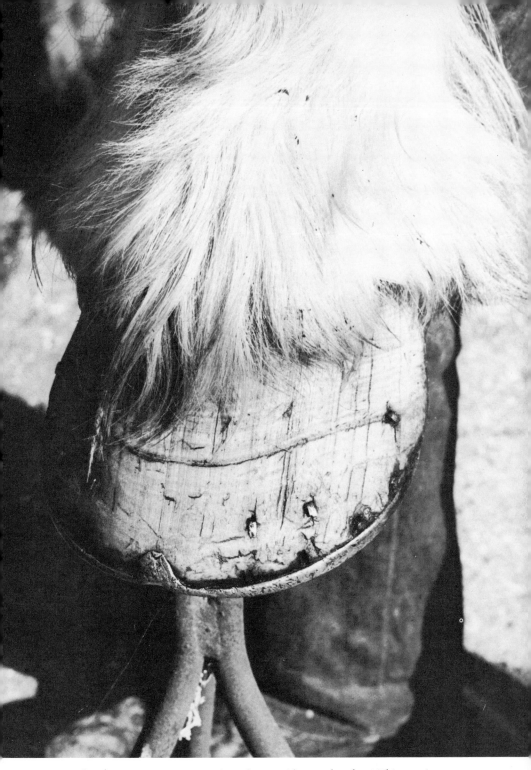

Not many beginners are going to acquire a horse with a perfect foot! This one is serviceable, but could do with some attention

horse. But you must leave all these matters, if they arise, to the vet. Let us think of the foot itself, which you must look at daily and which, as long as you keep it healthy, will help to prevent numerous other troubles arising.

The horny wall of the hoof, growing round the pedal bone, is a big fingernail or toenail. It grows like a nail. Your own nail is more or less insensitive: your horse's, being so immensely thick and large, is very insensitive. You can hammer nails into it, and he will not mind. But your nail also has a 'quick', and you need no telling how sensitive that is. Likewise your horse's foot has a quick.

The whole of his weight, and the weight of his load, are borne on the horny wall and the V-shaped bars. The sole is also horny, but does not come in contact with the ground. The frog and the bulbs of the heel are rather like the fleshy part of our middle finger or the pads of a dog or cat, acting as shock absorbers and anti-slip cushions. The fissures between the bars and the frog, and the cleft of the frog, are sensitive. Together they form the quick.

The foot, obviously, should be the right size for the horse, the right shape (not flat nor narrow) and at the right angle, ideally forming at the front a straight line with the pastern (not upright nor over-sloping). If your horse's foot meets these requirements, that is fine. If not, you could buy another horse. You can do nothing else about it, and even the greatest genius among farriers can do only a little to correct the trouble. But you can do a lot to force the foot into an even worse state than nature created it, and that is what you must take care to avoid.

If your horse were destined to spend all his life on the surfaces where his species evolved, the walls and bars would be kept to a regular length because they would wear down as fast as they grow, and grow as fast as they wear down. But the walls would become torn or split or utterly and completely worn away if you put him often on hard unnatural surfaces and did not put shoes on him.

The metal shoe of course wears down also, but very slowly. Yet its presence does not prevent the horn from growing. Since the walls are greater in circumference at the bottom than at the top, they will gradually, as they grow, spread over and around the shoe. If you want an inkling of how painful that can be, give up cutting your toenails for Lent, wear tightish shoes, never take them off and spend the whole of Easter Day walking about. So you must get the farrier to remove the shoes at intervals of about four to six weeks (have a look at the feet, and see) and to trim the walls to their proper length. He will then either replace the shoes or, if they are found to be too worn, fit new ones.

Unfortunately, there are very few farriers these days who actually hand-make shoes. Unless you are exceedingly lucky, every one within a day's march round you will supply ready-made ones. These come of course in a whole range of sizes. A good farrier will do very well with them, but a second-rater will fall to the temptation of trying to make the hoof fit the best available shoe he has. He probably does not have many customers with horse's feet as large as yours, and he may be at something of a loss. He might not even know as much about the correct length of the foot as he should. If, for example, the foot is allowed gradually to grow too long, the angle of the pastern will be thrown out. The shoe may perfectly fit the foot, but the foot itself should not be as it is.

This is really a serious matter. Not many of us humans need a surgical boot or shoe, but many have some little peculiarity which a top-class bespoke shoemaker could counteract. How much better we would be for that – even though few of us these days give our feet a real test. The nearest equivalent, in human terms, to what we ask a cart-horse to do is the tremendous thumping and battering to which a top-class fast bowler, playing cricket six or seven days a week, subjects his feet. You should do all you can to find the best farrier in your area, persuade him to take you on, and do nothing to offend him.

The frog will take care of itself – provided that the horn is not allowed to grow too long, in which case the frog will not touch the ground at all and will therefore be unable to do its job. The sole must not on any account be cut, though loose bits can be gently helped to flake away.

The ordinary shoe has four nail-holes on the outside and three on the inside. It also has a clip at the front, or one on each side of the front. A fullered shoe, with a groove running right round the bottom, helps to prevent slipping, especially when the groove becomes full of soil and grit.

Bevelled shoes are heavier than ordinary ones, and therefore make the horse pick his feet up high and slightly shorten his step. This encourages impressive action at a show, but is of no value for everyday purposes. In fact, bevels make the work more onerous – and danger-ous. Because their outside measurement is bigger than that of the hoof, and they have a sharp edge, they are liable to cut the inside of the other leg. This type of shoe has to be specially made, because you cannot buy ready-made ones. So, even if your blacksmith can make them, they will cost more, and take longer to put on because they have to be fitted especially carefully. Do not bother with them if you are going only to local shows. On the other hand, a good new set might last the whole show season if your horse is not going on the roads and he walks reasonably evenly. It is your choice because, although bevels used to be essential when showing a horse in good-class company, the judges nowadays are asked not to penalise the use of ordinary ones.

There is no law to say that your horse must wear shoes. If you have an in-foal mare not working at all, she can be unshod. But she may need her feet trimmed up. It all depends on the degree to which her temporary life-style will keep her feet just right without any help.

Examine your horse's feet daily, or as often as you can: for example, at grooming, and especially on his return from work. Stand as close as possible to him, facing his rear end, run your hand down from his shoulder or from his rump to his fetlock, and press your shoulder against him. This will encourage him to allow his foot to be lifted. If you seize it suddenly and start heaving, he will think your aim is to make him fall over.

What do you see? Dung stuck in there? Mud? Get it out with a hoof pick, for if it remains the foot might become inflamed and develop a disease called thrush, especially if the muck is impregnated with ammonia from his urine. Or is there a stone wedged in the frog, or stuck in the muck, to cause bruising and lameness? Operate the pick from heel to toe, not in the reverse direction, unless you want to run the risk of damaging the sole or frog. While you are about it, examine the outer walls for any slight crack in the surface, which might be the beginning of sandcrack. Check that the shoes are all right, and consider how soon it will be before your horse needs his feet trimmed.

If your horse goes lame, see if there is something in his foot. Then check whether a nail has shifted. Feel down his leg. Is there a swelling? Has he banged it? Has he been kicked? Whereabouts is it? Has he got a splint? (This is a bony enlargement from the cannon bone as we said earlier.) It could be serious. On the other hand, a horse might be lame one day and all right the next. Watch to see if the lameness is intermittent. If so, you will end by ringing the vet, but it is probably not urgent. Is there abnormal heat? If so, you could try using a cold water hose twice a day for twenty minutes to reduce it. But if you are in any doubt, call the vet.

A slight lameness is not always apparent except to the experienced man. When the beginner does spot it, he thinks it may just be stiffness. So it may, but then again it might not. It could be difficult to diagnose: for all he knows the trouble might be in the shoulder, not in the leg at all.

There is one disease of the foot which will send you rushing to the telephone. This is laminitis, or founder, or fever in the feet. It is an inflammation of the sensitive part, but the symptoms are everywhere, and often alarming. Suddenly, your horse will refuse to move. He will breathe fast. He will have a high temperature. He tries to stand on his heels. He is in great pain. His feet are hot. Oddly, all sorts of different things might cause all this, from over-long standing or walking on hot roads to excitement, or from over-feeding and under-exercise to over-work (unlikely nowadays!), or stupid attempts to pare the frog or ham-handed rasping and slicing at the walls. Contact your vet.

Send for the vet if there is anything which worries you, but be sensible. You probably do not understand your own legs very well, but you do not call the doctor for an attack of cramp or pins and needles, or to remove a stone from your shoe. But if your feet go purple and you cannot put them on the ground without screaming, you do seek help.

Grease is a trouble which especially affects the hairy-legged type of cart-horses. It begins as a discharge, with a very nasty smell, from the back of the pastern where the hair grows thickest, and more commonly on the hind-legs. As the trouble increases, thick growths develop – picturesquely known as 'grapes', which accurately describes their appearance but nothing else. The horse does not like having grease. The irritation causes him to keep banging his leg against a wall, or to rub his legs together. He may end by going lame. Once it gets a real hold, you will never cure grease, but you can keep it within bounds if you get your vet to make you up a lotion. Some people used to use pig oil and sulphur, but do not experiment. Ask the vet to change the prescription occasionally, for that often helps.

When you think it is necessary, smear the horn of the feet with hoof oil. This keeps it from becoming brittle, and makes it look nice, too. The natural oils of the foot are sufficient for horses in the wild, but shoeing, hard surfaces and other artificialities combine to make brittle feet a hazard of domestication. Make sure that what you buy is not just a varnish. This is cosmetic, but bad for the feet because it does the opposite of what an oil achieves. Some hoof oils have tar in them, but the tweedy cart-horse does not wear city suits and should not have black feet.

If you are taking your horse to a show, that is a good time to use hoof oil. And rub the clips of the shoes with emery paper to make them shine. Some people even paint them silver. And do make sure the feet are clean before you go in the ring. When the judge picks them up, he is not being curious about the sort of soil you have at home. He wants to see the feet. If consolidated clay meets his eye, he will learn more about you than about your horse.

# 5
# Work on the Farm

No one needs to be told the work a horse can do in town. It simply consists of hauling things about or delivering them. And the type of vehicle to be used will depend on the nature of the business. In any case a professional foreman will be employed. But the farmer contemplating the possibility of a horse or two is faced with a much more complex situation, and may need some encouragement in his seeming folly. So our shortest chapter is devoted to him.

### What the horse can do

Carting jobs, pure and simple, are ideal - hauling out hay for the cows and young stock; picking up animal manure and taking it out; and so on. The horse can often do this while the tractor is on tougher work. The wife of one well-organised farmer happens to love Shetland ponies, and keeps two. So, if a job such as carting a few bales of hay arises, she claims it. The ponies get their exercise pulling their little trolley. Since they subsist on a couple of hours' grazing in every twenty-four (any more than that in spring or summer would be too much for their health), their labour is virtually free. The basic principle is well illustrated on this farm, which also has several Shires. If it is unthrifty to use a tractor for what a cart-horse does more cheaply, why use a cart-horse for something which your two tough little Shetlands can do cheaper still?

In partnership with the tractor, you might consider carting fertiliser or seed for your drills. This might release your second tractor, which ought to be earning money doing the hard work. There is hardly a place for horses in the corn-harvest, but for potatoes it depends on your system. Horses can cart bags or, for that matter, loose potatoes.

A horse and cart can turn in a fraction of the length required by a tractor and trailer. There are lots of places on many farms - some of them relics of the former horse age - where for this reason it is easier to use a horse in doing a clearing-out job.

On all sorts of start–stop work, horses are particularly economic – erecting fencing, putting feed into a number of mangers, or anything else which involves constant jumping up and down from a tractor. Such jobs are often done at great expense by two men. This is unnecessary if you have a horse. Any routine task he will learn quickly, and stop at the right time and place without even being told.

Many tractor jobs can be started, if the land is unfit, with the horses – or else finished with them if the ground gets too wet and heavy before you have finished. Even ploughing. Horse-ploughing used to be reckoned at an acre a day but it would be absurd to talk about that. (In any case, it was not easy to keep up even that average, if the truth were known.) We mean something rather different.

Start your day by feeding the horses. By the time the milking or other jobs are done, the horses will have digested their food. You cannot do your ploughing with the tractor because the land is too wet, so take the horses out and make a start with them. Go on using them at odd times – the second half of the morning, the otherwise idle afternoon. Then, as soon as the ground is dry enough, the tractor can get to work on the bulk of it. It may be surprising how far ahead you have got, instead of being behind. And it is better than staying indoors biting your nails and wondering if conditions will ever be right again. Also there may be certain patches of ground that are a perpetual nuisance to you – they always lie wet until too late. Why not turn these over with the horses? Do not be hidebound.

Since you can get on the ground earlier with horses in the spring, and can carry on later at the back-end, what about harrowing in the winter corn with horses, or chain harrowing it in the spring? Two good horses can do fifteen to twenty acres a day. You can also top dress your early bite, if you have a fertiliser drill, when conditions are wet. It is much cheaper to spread fertiliser or weed-killer with a horse than from a helicopter. The horse does little more damage than the aircraft, and does not squirt the spray into hedges, roads or your neighbour's lupins.

It is not fanciful to suggest that you do a little hay-raking. With hay the price it now is, it could be worth your while to save a lot that would otherwise go to waste. You will soon rake up enough to feed your horses. As the advertisements like to say, save £££! However, do not try to invent jobs. Do not use the horse simply because you have him. Live, and work, from day to day. Do not worry if there are days when your horse is doing nothing much.

It might be a good idea to take counsel from your Trusty Adviser.

Side-raking hay with a Bamford's FGN side-rake. This is one of the many useful jobs a horse can do. Note the ear-caps to keep out flies

Get him along, point out everything you do on the farm, how you do it, where the buildings are, and so on. Ask him how he would fit horses into this pattern of work. He might think of a lot of things which had not occurred to you.

## Vehicles

You can cart things round your farm, or even along the public highway, in any odd-looking contraption you like. The only considerations, apart from your pride, are that it should be convenient for the work you need to do and that it should make the least troublesome load for your horse. If it has two wheels, you can bow to tradition to the extent of calling it a cart. If it is a tractor trolley fitted with shafts, it would be going a little far to refer to it as a waggon, simply because it has four wheels. Call it a trolley.

A trolley can be a very useful means of transport, but remember that a four-wheeled vehicle requires more horse-power to move it than a two-wheeled one, and this is accentuated when you are not on a road or other smooth firm surface. A low vehicle is obviously easier for loading and unloading than a high one, but if you want a tipping cart you will have to sacrifice this advantage. Rubber-tyred wheels do not sink into the ground like the old wooden ones, but they do slide about. Wooden wheels roll on very well and last a long time but they also bring your cart up higher than you probably like.

Even if you possess an authentic traditional cart, you will probably not want to use it in daily work. It is too valuable to be knocked about, so keep it for shows. And we could scarcely imagine your finding suitable work for a waggon. But this is not a book about carts and waggons. If we tried to say anything really helpful about them, there would be no pages left for the horses. So let us confine our thoughts to a few general principles. And let us start by assuming that you are looking out for a vehicle that you can take to shows.

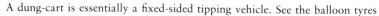

A dung-cart is essentially a fixed-sided tipping vehicle. See the balloon tyres

The scotch cart is the most useful general-purpose farm cart. It can be made to tip, and may have side-boards. Note the prop-sticks for leaving the cart loaded

If you are ambitious enough to propose exhibiting a pair of horses, have a waggon: otherwise, choose a cart. Your decision will also be influenced by the cost of transport. For example, if you had a burning desire to create a sensation by showing a timber waggon drawn by three horses (or six, or nine), you might be under a similar handicap to that of the musician who plays the harp and drives a Mini.

The easiest thing to do is to have a new vehicle made specially for you. All you require for this is the money and enough sense to discover your nearest expert builder whose knowledge and craftsmanship match each other. You do not want to pay a great sum for something that will make you look like a circus act. Discuss with him the possibilities of dung carts and scotch carts, or even some sort of farm float, or speak to him of waggons. He will create to your specification but, if you want to win at shows, do not ask him to incorporate your own idiosyncrasies or idiocies into the design. Let it be authentic. (Incidentally, there is a sharp distinction at shows between trade and agricultural vehicles – see Chapter 8, page 162.)

Are you, instead, going to renovate an old vehicle? If so, do not superimpose your flights of fancy upon the basic wreck that you have purchased. Renovation should be restoration. For this reason, beware of a vehicle which has already been done up by someone else. He may have done it all wrong. Furthermore, be cautious about something which may seem unusual enough to be interesting, such as a vehicle with vintage rubber tyres of the old 'balloon' type. You will perhaps be the only person who has failed to realise the impossibility of finding anything of the right size to replace them.

Restoration of course includes repainting. Do not try this yourself, unless you happen to be a coach-painter. It is not only a matter of whether you can do all those wriggly lines, the skills required being somewhat greater than in DIY. The correct colours are also important and these are often very localised. If your vehicle is new, make sure that they conform to your district, or even your parish. If it is an old one from a far distant county, and the paint has all worn away or you suspect that it has not been repainted correctly, try to find out what is proper there. Much of the old horse tradition may have been lost, but there is no virtue in heedlessly throwing away what remains.

To return to our original subject, the working horse, how about a hitch cart? This American invention is not really a cart at all, but a means of enabling implements to be used by someone driving horses, instead of walking behind them. There are only a few in this country. The reason why the idea was not adopted here is that in the old days the Americans had unlimited acreage, but were short of labour. We

(*opposite*) A wide variety of trailed implements can be towed behind a hitch cart. The construction of one of these is a matter of individual taste

(*below*) A slurry cart explains itself, but it can also be used as a water-cart. This also has prop-sticks, so that it can be gradually loaded over a period of time

had labour in plenty, but not the acreage. In any case, our grandfathers believed it was immoral for their men to ride at work, when they were perfectly capable of walking. Times are different now.

A hitch cart is basically a pair of wheels and an axle, with a seat arranged on top, and a pole. Two, three, or six (or forty) horses can then be hitched to tow an implement behind it – harrows, rollers, four-wheeled trailers: in fact, anything towable.

It will have to be constructed to your specification, but this is not difficult. There are two main essentials. Firstly, it should be high enough in the seat to enable you to look down through the horses, instead of looking up through them, as when you are walking. Secondly, you need the draw-bar as far under the axle as possible, so that the whole thing does not tip when pulling. It is best mounted on rubber wheels, but it can be on wooden ones. Any old axle and wheels will do. There are just two snags. It needs level ground. And, if you are working the land, it requires a bigger headland than is normal for horses.

Nowadays, for those with 'hobby' horses or with horses that are only occasionally worked and need to be exercised, a hitch cart could be a special attraction. You can exercise all your horses together, while having a ride yourself. This is particularly useful if you are busy, lazy or not in good trim. One man even fitted his hitch cart with a bench seat from an old car. He and his wife and child all went for a stately ride together, exercising the horses in moderate comfort. On public roads, his wife felt superior to other wives in their family saloons. She rode higher, and they looked up to her.

## Implements

A certain dismal day in the wet June of 1980 produced something to cheer the horseman's heart. The first items of brand-new horse-machinery seen for many years in this country were demonstrated to a select few.

Imported from Poland, where these things are still extensively used, a rubber-tyred mower and a hay-turner successfully dealt with a modern grass crop. A fertiliser-spreader was due to follow and by the time you read these words there may be other implements, too.

As we write, there is also a good prospect of a new British-made manure-spreader being put on the market – an ideal job for horses. The chief obstacle in the way of anyone wishing to do a limited amount of horse-husbandry is at last being removed.

Chain-harrowing, using a hitch cart

If, however, you are one of those who are prepared to search around for old stuff, or who enjoy doing so, it can still be found. It is often easier to find an outstandingly good implement than to persuade the owner to part with it. You can spend hours trying to talk something out of people, even though they do not really want to keep it. They might ask a ridiculous price 'because it is an antique'. You can also waste time and money chasing wild geese. You are told on the telephone that 'it worked perfectly the last time it was used'. When you arrive, you find a ruin. A shed has fallen on it, and they have not told you. On the other hand, families have been known to give a good implement to a man simply because he actually proposes to use it: 'Father would have liked the idea.'

Rolling a seed-bed with a pair of horses and a tractor-roller. To ease the horse's burden, the draw-bar is supported by a carrying-wheel

With anything that has working parts, the commonest trouble is that, in days when horses were being superseded, someone cut the shafts off and used the implement behind a tractor. He would go at a much greater speed than it was designed for, and rip its guts out. You find the bearings worn, and so on. The ideal items are those which never did much work with horses and have never been tractor-pulled.

Try to discover the good makes of various implements, and the good and bad models of each. When you restore something, repaint

it in the correct colour. All Ransome ploughs, for example, were blue. Do not paint yours pink because you like that colour.

It is a big mistake to keep on buying old broken-down equipment; you will never restore it all. And it is easy to get carried away at auction sales. Lines and lines of old things are laid out, many of them nothing more than heaps of rubbish, and yet they all seem to find purchasers.

If you are not fond of restoring wrecks, or have no time to go looking for them, you can of course buy from someone whose main enjoyment is derived from that part of it. But if he has tinkered with something or restored it, make certain he has done it properly, and watch that he does not have an inflated notion of its value.

A few comments might be useful about some of the old items that can be found. Nearly all *ploughs* will be Ransomes, which were all good. For some models, it is difficult to get new shares, but the local blacksmith can make you coulters and other parts can be made or adapted. *Cultivators* are somewhat rare, but you may come across one. It is still possible to buy new chain and disc *harrows*.

There are plenty of corn and root *drills*, many of which came from America in the Second World War. An old-fashioned agricultural engineer might also have parts lying around. Or you can buy two to make one, though the same parts are of course likely to have worn on both.

Your *roller* can be a tractor-roller. To take the weight off the horses, you can put a front wheel on the draw-bar, but do not go on the road or down a hill because it will run into the horses. A proper shafted horse-roller is better, of course.

*Hoes* vary. Some you cannot get new tines for, but it is possible to improvise. *Slurry carts* can easily be made. *Manure-spreaders* were

A modern British-made horse-drawn dung-spreader. The first new model to be introduced for many years, it can also be adapted easily for use with a tractor (*Colin and Janet Fry*)

Three machines now imported from Poland. The mowing-machine, fertiliser-distributor and hay-turner are all on rubber tyres (*Colin and Janet Fry*)

mostly torn to pieces by tractors, so the new-made ones will be welcome.

It is probably best to buy a new Polish *mower*, because the density of the grass grown nowadays is enormously increased and much more power is needed for a cut than was required when the old ones were made. If you must have an old one, remember that there used to be one-horse and two-horse models, and also engine-driven mowers pulled by one horse. These are tiring for him because of the vibration, but the higher knife-speed usually means that they can cut thick grass.

Imported *hay-turners* are similarly your best bet. Better seed and the closer cut obtained by modern mowers have enormously increased the yield, and the old turners will have difficulty in working properly. However, there were some very good ones, doing their work better than the tractor-drawn models.

There are plenty of *rakes* about, and they do a good job. Many are now without shafts, so you will have to see to that. And if you want to make all your hay loose, there are a few *hay sweeps* to be found. But then you will want an elevator. Surprisingly, old-fashioned *hay loaders* can still be found in good condition.

*Binders* can also be located, including some very good ones made by Massey-Harris. A binder is wanted if wheat is grown for thatch. You can also track down *potato bulkers*.

But let us finish here, omitting other localised types of equipment. Doing really useful jobs with horses is going to depend, in most cases, on the new implements and machinery. But the enthusiast for things rescued from a hedge or a cob-webbed barn will still be able to indulge his hobby.

# 6

# Harness

You must have a halter to lead your horse with, and tie him up. Then, for work, he is bound to wear a collar and a bridle, whatever else he is going to have. We then come to the three types of harness that are required at different times – beginning with the most complicated, because the whole thing is easier to understand that way round. After that, we think about the items you can add to basic harness for show and decorative purposes. Finally, there are some remarks about looking after it all. Incidentally, do not despair about obtaining it in the first place. You can buy it second-hand or, if you have the money, you can have it made new.

### Halters

To tie a horse up in a stall, you need either a leather head collar or a Yorkshire halter. The former exists in many patterns and may have superior brass-mountings or tinny ones. The latter, however, is made of hemp, is light, lies flat and therefore can also be easily worn under a bridle.

An adjustable rope halter is also useful because it will fit a foal or a horse with either a small or large head. It should have a shank long enough to enable the horse to be tied up. This should be threaded through a ring attached to the edge of the manger and then through a sinker or chock – a block of wood about four inches in diameter with a hole through it. The end of the rope is then knotted underneath the sinker. In cases of emergency (for example, fire and terrified horse) rope is better than a chain, because it can be cut.

If you are good at splicing ropes, or if you are lucky enough to number an old sailor among your friends, you (or he) can make dozens of rope halters. You must be careful that there are no slipknots, and that the throat lash is not too tight. On the other hand, your horse must not be able to get out of it. If he does that once, he is liable to go on trying.

For leading a horse about or showing him in hand, you need a white halter of either cotton or hemp. These have no throat-lash. You can also get nylon ones, but some people do not like them. In an emergency, you can construct a makeshift halter out of a bit of baler twine.

## Collar and hames

The horse wears a collar; the collar is fitted with hames; the hames are linked by chains to the load. So the horse never pulls anything, but pushes into the collar.

The collar consists of two parts, stitched together. The body is of straw padding enclosed in special collar cloth, and the outside (but not the inside, which lies against the horse's neck) is covered with leather. The roll, a leather tube tightly packed with straw, goes round the front of the body of the collar.

Collars are shaped in such a way as not to cause pressure where it is not needed. For example, the bottom is clear of the throat. It is also, of course, wider at the bottom than at the top. Consequently, it will not pass over the horse's head, unless he happens to have a massive neck compared with his head, as some do. But this does not mean you are faced with the ship-in-a-bottle problem. All you do is to put the collar on over the head upside down, and then turn it the right way up.

The size of his collar is far more important to the horse than the size of your collar is to you. If yours is too small, you will not get it round your neck. You can get too small a collar round a horse's neck, but too high up. When he pushes into it with a heavy load behind, he will choke. If his collar is all right for length, but too narrow, it will be agony. If it is too big, his misery will be grievous, for it will slide about. If your collar is too big, you merely look odd.

A horse collar is measured, not by passing a tape round it, but according to its length from top to bottom and side to side. You can test if it is right by seeing whether the back of it, all round, is in the correct place and then manually checking the front. If your four fingers extended together can pass into the front of the collar at the bottom, and if one finger can be inserted into the front at each side, all is well. Should your horse gain or lose flesh, the collar will be too small or too big. If it is the right size, but not a very even fit at various points, soak it in water overnight, put it on next day and then, when it has been properly adapted, take it off and dry it out.

To prevent injury, any halter must be knotted like this before tying a horse up

The size of a collar is determined by the inside measurement

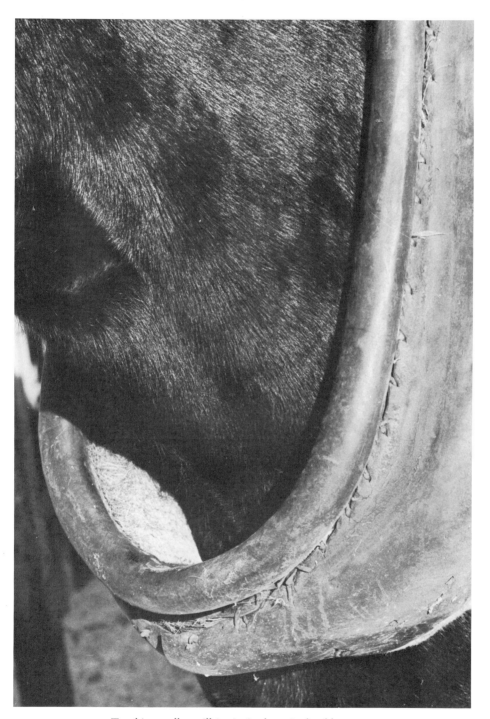

Too big a collar will 'wring' a horse's shoulders

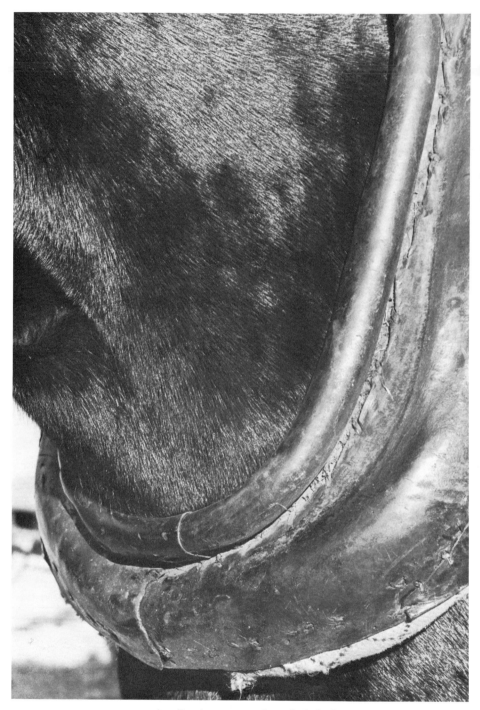

A collar that is too tight will choke him

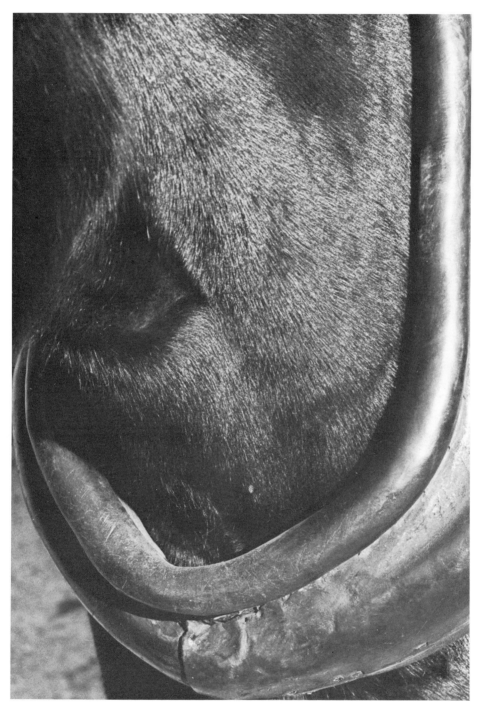

This collar is just right!

There are several specialist types of collar. Heavy peaked collars with high tops are favoured in Scotland. Pipe collars are specially shaped at the bottom for horses that are liable to choke easily. The open collar, originally invented for horses that would not allow anything to be passed over their heads, is pushed upwards on to the neck and the top is then buckled together with two straps. These became popular in the South-West of England. For horses that will not wear a neck collar, or that on medical grounds cannot, the alternative is the breast collar. This is a bit low for efficient draught in shaft work, but is all right for most farming operations.

The hames are two shaped steel rods which fit into the groove between the body and the roll of the collar, up each side of the horse's neck. They are linked together at the bottom by a chain and hook, and at the top by a strap and buckle. Above this strap, each hame extends upwards into the air for some inches, and this part is called the crook. On each hame, there is an iron hook to accommodate one end of a chain. A short chain, the 'tug', links, at its other end, to the shaft: a long chain is used in trace or plough harness.

Hames may also be made of wood, or of wood cased in iron, but these are rare nowadays. Brass hames, often favoured for show purposes, are not strong enough for heavy work. Hames also vary in pattern, and there are many different ways that they are fitted together at the bottom and joined at the top. In fact, variation is the key word whenever one attempts to describe any part of the harness. Every region of the country has some sort of speciality.

Just as the collar must fit the horse, the hames must be the right size and shape to fit the collar perfectly. They should be taken off the collar before the collar is removed from the horse. Some people used to argue that it was best to leave the hames on even when stored, on the grounds that they kept the collar the right shape. But this is the only argument in favour and it is a weak one.

### Bridle, bit and reins

The horse wears a bridle; the bridle contains the bit; the bit is directly linked to the man behind by means of reins or lines. So, by pulling one of these, the man can inform the horse whether he is to turn left or right. By pulling both or by flicking them, he can tell him to stop or move forward.

So that it may stay on the horse's head and keep the bit in its correct position, the bridle consists of cheek-straps (with blinkers, unless it is an 'open' bridle); nose-band; throat-strap; head-strap; and brow-band. Bit-straps from a ring connecting the nose-band and cheek-straps are attached to the rings of the bit, to which all types of rein are attached.

The various patterns of bridle, blinkered and open, are more numerous than can be listed in a small space. The merits and demerits of the open bridle have been argued for generations and the points at issue tend to become very technical. We must content ourselves with the fact that you will find blinkers customary among cart-horse men. Just two other varieties of bridle do perhaps require mention. Firstly, the full-faced bridle, in addition to the parts listed above as essential, has a broad band coming down the front of the horse's face, from head-strap to brow-band and down to the nose-band. Secondly, in the loose-cheek bridle, the cheek-strap does not help to bear the weight of the bit, and this is severe on the mouth of a young horse.

Your main concern should be to avoid, if possible, cluttering up your horse with too heavy a bridle. Some weigh as little as three pounds (admittedly, open bridles), and others as much as seven. It must be strong, especially for team-work, but it is better if it is also light. You will find, when or if you have the chance of trying several kinds, that it is possible to alter the appearance of a horse's head, for better or worse, by the style of bridle he wears. Some men look good in a top hat, and silly in a tweed cap: others, the reverse.

The throat-lash should be tight enough only to keep the bridle firmly on the horse's head. It is not a device for throttling him. If you concede that he has, like you, a windpipe, nerves, muscles and so on, you will do all you can to make the whole contraption as comfortable as possible. It is useful to remember that the centre of the blinker should cover the centre of the eye.

Bits are even more confusing than bridles in the multiplicity of their styles and patterns, but very many of the designs that have been marketed have added absolutely nothing to the art of driving or riding. All that you need is a plain iron snaffle or straight bar bit. This comprises a ring on each side of the mouth connected by an unjointed mouthpiece resting on the tongue and bars – that is, the gums behind the incisor teeth and in front of the molars. It works on the corners of the horse's mouth, and should therefore touch them, but without being so far back that it wrinkles them. The important thing is that the bit should be of the right size, and perfectly fitted to his mouth. If you have ever tried wearing someone else's dentures, you will appreciate what we mean. Some expert town-users employ a

Liverpool curb-bit. This works on a different principle, but you do not need to involve yourself with that. (Another sort of bit is used in breaking a young horse. See Chapter 7, page 134.)

Remember that the horse is not a machine. The bit does fulfil the function of a car's steering wheel, and of its brakes, too. But it rests on a sensitive tongue and works on sensitive lips. The lighter your touch, the better for the horse – and the better for you. If you are rough and heavy-handed, his mouth will become 'hard' and you will not be able to manage him easily. It is important to be aware that the pull on the off-side ring has a more severe effect than an apparently equal pull on the near side.

You have a voice, and the horse has ears. He can learn to understand what you say. The better your oral communication, the less you need to pull on your horse's mouth.

There are three types of rein:

(i) Reins to control and direct the horse when you are behind him, either walking or in a vehicle. For horses harnessed to waggons or

A collection of bits: from top left, reading down, are a Liverpool bit with curb chain, snaffle bit with T-piece, and snaffle straight-bar bit. Top right and below are a breaking bit with keys, a straight-bar bit with hook, a jointed twisted snaffle bit, and a plain jointed snaffle bit

carts, the driving reins are of leather if you are on the road or at a show, but of rope if you are working on the farm. For horses harnessed to machinery and implements, rope is always used, and the 'reins' are then called lines.

Rope is less slippery if the weather is wet and your hands are muddy. It is also cheaper. A third advantage could be a vital one. Your reins or lines must be not only of the same length but also of exactly the right length. If they are too short and you have to stand or walk at an angle of forty-five degrees to reach the ends, the dangers are obvious. If they are too long, your demise might be just as sudden, for the ends might trail on the ground or you might be foolish enough to roll the spare amount round your hands. However, three separate jobs in one single day might require reins or lines of three different lengths. Ropes can be given half-hitches to shorten them as much or as little as you like. An extra length can even be tied on.

Sometimes, you might find you need a length of rope to secure something you want to put in your cart. If you happen to be at the furthermost extremity of your estate, you can save yourself walking across the field to the house by using a rein, if it is of rope, and then lead your horse home.

Between the bit-ring and your hands, you will need one or more convenient rings through which the reins or lines can pass, in order to keep them away from the horse's legs if they (the reins) go slack. The best position for these rings will vary according to the height of your hands, because you will want the reins or lines to run as straight as possible. When you are sitting on a high seat driving a waggon, the angle formed at the bit will be above the horizontal. When you are walking behind a plough the angle will be below it. If the reins travel up and down in a series of angles before they reach your hands, you will be tugging on them harder than you should, and with less certainty of how strong a message the horse is receiving. Suggestions about the route which the reins or lines can best follow between the bit-rings and the hands are given when we discuss each particular type of harness.

(ii) A rein to prevent the horse lowering its head (say, to eat), which might be dangerous. This is the bearing-rein, which runs from one bit-ring round one of the hame-crooks and back to the other bit-ring. Farmers at work loop the bearing-rein over the off-side hame-crook because they might want to use the near-side one as a convenient peg to hang things on – their coat or their food. Town drivers of course

This is the safe way to shorten your lines

could keep such items as these on the vehicle, and generally used the near-side crook for the bearing-rein.

Bearing-reins often used to be criticised as being cruel. So they were and so they are – if they are short enough to force the horse to carry his head agonisingly and immovably high simply for sake of appearance. They are not designed for that. They are intended to prevent him putting his head too low, which is a different matter. Even so, sometimes the horse has to be 'unreined'. For example, he cannot pull a heavy load up a steep slope unless he can put his head down.

(iii) A rein to lead a horse. The leading-rein is only for shaft work, and is therefore discussed later.

A dangerous way to shorten your lines. When he trips over the dangling ends (or when the horse runs away), this man will not be able to free his hands

## Shaft harness

Carts, one-horse and some two-horse waggons, rollers, mowers, hay-turners, manure and other distributors, and some hoes, have shafts. A shaft-horse wears a saddle, of which the main function, performed by means of a chain running across it, is to take the weight of the shafts and hold them to a suitable height. In the case of carts, this is particularly vital, since, if the vehicle is on a downward slope and its load happens to be well forward, it is not merely a matter of dead weight but of a downward thrust. One does not want the horse's efficiency, or his comfort, to be impeded by an immensely increased burden upon his neck.

Nor, on the other hand, does one want the shafts to rise when the horse is going uphill, and force him on tip-toes at the very time he needs to plant his feet firmly and exert his strength. Therefore he also wears a belly band underneath him, in the form of a strap which can be buckled on to the shafts.

A better way of expressing the main purpose of these contraptions would therefore be to say that they are the means whereby a two-wheeled vehicle can be balanced. The importance of balance was once demonstrated by someone who thoughtlessly placed a mare in front of a stallion which happened to be harnessed to a loaded cart, earning an honest living and keeping fit. Surprised and pleased, the horse reared up, but could not come down again because he had taken the shafts and belly band with him, and the whole load slipped to the back of the cart.

The saddle consists of a comfortably shaped pad, not too big for your horse, nor too small, on to which is fitted a convex wooden frame or 'tree' covered in a housing of leather. Across the tree, at right angles to the line of the horse's back, is the bridge, a channel in which the back-chain or ridger can rest. One end of this ridger is often permanently fixed to the off-side shaft of a cart and is therefore not really part of the harness. (It may even be permanently fixed at both ends, as we shall see.) Leather flaps are sometimes needed, nailed to

(*opposite above*) This horse is hitched all wrong. For example, the shafts are too low, the tugs too long and the breeching and belly band too slack. And the reins are hanging inside the shafts

(*opposite below*) Here we have a vast improvement on the effort shown in the previous picture

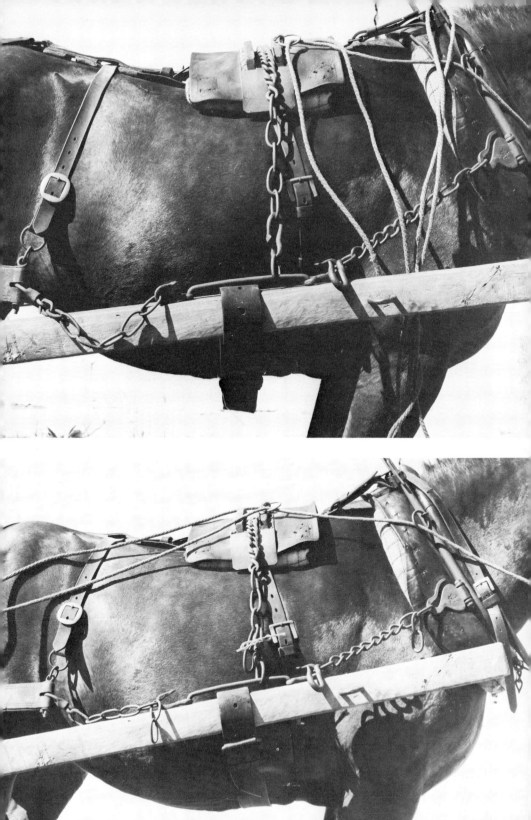

the bottom edge of the tree on each side, to prevent the horse's sides being rubbed by the chain.

To prevent it slipping backwards or the collar forwards, the saddle is linked to the collar by two meeter-straps which are buckled to the hames-strap, or by some other means on which we need not elaborate. To prevent it slipping sideways, there is a girth-strap (or pair of girth-straps) going under the body. And it cannot slip forwards because of the breeching. So the saddle's secondary function is to act as an essential link between the collar, by which the vehicle is moved forwards, and the breeching, which the horse uses to move it backwards, stop it, or prevent it running into his rear end when going downhill.

There are several distinct parts of the breeching. The crupper, attached to the saddle by a strap or leather loop, goes along the top of the horse's back to a point just forward of the tail. The loin- and hip-straps, as their names suggest, are suspended from the crupper down each side of the horse at two different points. They support the breech-band. This goes horizontally round his breech and the front ends are attached to the shafts by breeching-chains. It is this breech-band which, by leaning back against it, the horse uses as a brake and reversing device. It must therefore be of the right size for him. But so, of course, must be every other part of the harness.

(A word of explanation is needed about a cart-harness crupper. A true crupper reaches back much farther and ends in a loop through which the tail is placed. This is to provide an anchor to stop the forward parts of the harness from slipping forward too far. But in cart-harness such an anchor is unnecessary, since that function is performed by the breech-band. However, the cart-harness crupper does terminate, somewhat confusingly, in a loop like a true crupper. But this is only for storage purposes. The breeching is always left attached to the saddle and so, unless hooked up on a separate nail, would either trail on the ground or compel you to climb a ladder to hang the saddle higher than you could reach from the ground. Do not, therefore, attempt to pull your horse's tail up, bend it forward and stuff it through this loop. That would be as effective as trying to suspend your braces over your ears – they would not stay there long but, while they did, you would be in severe pain in at least two places.)

The driving-reins pass through rings on the hames and then through the rings on the saddle. In one or two localities you will find that neither hames nor saddle have rings on them. Perhaps folk there used to do a lot of walking and rarely had a ride. If you drive in these circumstances, you will have to run the reins over the hame-straps.

A leading-rein is for the use of a carter walking beside his horse, not driving, to give him quick control when needed. It runs straight from the bit-ring to the 'D' of the hip-strap, missing out the hame-ring, and should be free enough to lie outside the shaft.

*Shutting-in*

Let us assume that your horse is tied up in a stall with a Yorkshire halter. You want to put him to a cart. The following is a reasonable order of operations, though in points of detail there are some people who would do it slightly differently.

1. Take the collar. Untie the rope of the halter and put it through the collar. Put the collar over the horse's head.

2. If it is a young horse, tie him up again. An old one will stand quietly while he is being harnessed.

3. Turn the collar the right way up, remembering to pull the mane hair out from underneath it.

4. Fix the hames to the collar, and put the tug chains on the hames if they are not already attached.

5. Put on the saddle and breeching. Girth up, and buckle the meeter-strap. Always harness from the near side.

6. When you are ready to take the horse out, untie him, leave the halter on and put on the bridle. (With the halter still on, you can tie him up whenever you want.)

7. Attach the reins to the bit-rings, pass them through the collar-rings, and coil them neatly on the near-side hame-crook.

8. Back the horse out of the stall, and get him facing the doorway. Make sure he is at right angles to it and facing the middle of the opening before you lead him out. When experienced, he may be able to walk out on his own, but to start with he may bump his harness into the door-frame or even get it hooked up on something.

9. Take the horse to the cart and place him so that he is exactly in front of the shafts – with his back to them, of course. (A horse should never be shut in facing the cart.) Make certain that the horse is properly aligned to the shafts. If he is too much to the off side, turn his head in that direction, which will cause him to move his quarters

round to the near side: and, of course, vice versa.

Your movements will depend on whether your vehicle is one which, when not in use, is left with its shafts pointing in the air (in which case the back-chain or ridger will probably be permanently fixed to them at both ends) or resting on the ground (in which case the belly-band may, or may not, be a permanent fixture and one end of the ridger may, or may not, be permanently fixed to the off-side shaft). We shall take the latter case first (10–14) and then describe the order of events for the former case.

10.   Make quite sure that, if the ridger is permanently fixed to the off-side shaft, it is lying outside the shaft, out of the way of the horse's feet.

11.   Pressing on the bridle, back the horse carefully between the shafts. If the belly-band is a permanent fixture, it will of course be on the ground and your horse will have to step over it. Watch that he does not get his heel hooked up in it. (If it is not a permanent fixture, you should of course have brought it with you.)

12.   Go to the off side. Lift the shafts and attach the off-side tug. (Not necessarily at its correct eventual link, as that will be put right later.) If yours is a young horse, you will have to get someone to hold his head, because he may not like all the weight of the shafts pulling down on one side of his collar. Now throw the ridger over the saddle so that it lies in the bridge channel. (Should one end of it not be already permanently fixed to the off-side shaft, you should of course first attach that end. Otherwise, throwing it over will be useless. You will have to go round the other side and pick it all up off the ground.)

13.   Go to the near side and fasten the ridger; fasten the tug chain; fasten the breeching-chain; and buckle on the near side of the belly-band (unless the whole thing is permanently fixed to the shafts).

14.   Go back to the off side and adjust the tug to the correct length; fasten the off-side breeching chain; do up the side of the belly-band (unless a permanent fixture).

---

Here are the procedures for 10–14 if the shafts are in the air:

10.   There is no check to be made if the ridger is permanently fixed at both ends to the shafts, because it is in the air.

11.   Back the horse to the correct positon.

12.   Go to the near side. Let the shafts down gently. If you have got

the horse exactly right, the ridger will come neatly into the bridge-channel. If it lands on top of his rump, you have made a hopeless mess of it. Move the horse and try again.

13. Stay on the near side and fasten the tug; fasten the breeching-chain; and buckle on the near side of the belly-band.

14. Go to the off side and fasten the tug; fasten the off side of the breeching-chain; and buckle on the off side of the belly-band.

---

15. Make certain that every buckle is fastened to the hole that enables the strap concerned to do its job correctly – tight enough, but not too tight. In harness properly suited to the horse, buckles should engage with more or less the middle holes of straps. (What happens if your horse gains flesh, or loses it? If you are having to use end-holes, the harness is clearly intended for a smaller horse than yours.)

16. Ensure that the ridger is lifting the shafts to the correct height. The tug needs to be very little out of the horizontal when the horse is pulling.

17. Check that the tugs and the breeching-chains are the same length on each side. You will probably have spare unused links. If there are several, you will have a lot of chain swinging and banging, but this can be overcome by crooking the end link on first and then the link you require afterwards – all the spare chain thus making a neat little loop.

18. See that the belly-band is not so slack that the horse might get a hind foot caught up in it if he happens to kick against a fly. A gap of about four inches between his belly and the band is about right. The belly-band has not got to fit against him. You are not trying to truss him up – it is there in case something makes the shafts rise. If they do, it is called into play only briefly because you will rectify whatever has happened to cause the shafts to rise up.

19. Uncoil the reins, which are already through their rings on the collar, and put them through the rings on the saddle, if there are any.

20. Up you get, and off you go! If your horse seems to be going badly, perhaps you have not hitched everything right after all.

Twenty operations, some of them multiple, for harnessing and shutting-in one horse! This is a daunting thought, and you may feel tempted to ask your wife to read them out while you struggle and sweat. But with a little practice you will find you can do it in no time at all.

## Going forwards and backwards

Remember that a gateway must be approached at right angles and in the middle, with the gate wide open. You do not want to take a gate-post with you, or leave a wheel behind. This is particularly to be remembered with waggons, because the distance between the horse's nose and the back of the vehicle is considerable; and, obviously, the rear wheels follow in the tracks of the front ones only when the vehicle is going in a straight line.

If you are about to go up a steep hill, ensure that your cart is not loaded tail-heavy. And you may have to unhook the bearing-reins. A waggon should have a roller-scotch, a little wooden cylinder rolling along behind the rear wheel, to prevent the vehicle rolling backwards if there is a stop.

If you are about to go downhill with a farm waggon, the drug bat (or drag shoe or skid-pan), slung by a chain on the near side, should be placed under the back wheel to act as a brake. A force-chain is also put round the wheel in case it jumps out of the skid-pan on a bump. Skid-pans are not popular with the authorities, and commercial waggons or drays have proper brakes.

When backing, you must go to your horse's head. Get the cart square to where you want to go, and then back straight in. To steer a waggon in reverse is more difficult, because, as with a motor-car, it is done with the front wheels. A waggon may have a full lock, three quarter, half or quarter lock, but the last two types are inconvenient because they need such a wide turning circle.

Some horses do not like backing. If this is due to fear, as a result of some unpleasant experience in the past, they must be treated with understanding and patience to try to give them confidence. But a 'shiverer' will never be able to back. If one has been palmed off on you, bad luck.

There are also horses which, for some reason best known to them-selves, try to back at what seems like 90 miles an hour. This is no less dangerous than frightening and is the only known emergency in which it is courageous to turn your back on the situation. Do this, and move forward. The horse will probably stop before he smashes up the cart. But as long as you are facing him he will continue to accelerate.

## Shutting-out

This more or less consists of doing things in the reverse order of shutting-in. If your horse is young, you should certainly have someone to hold his head. And, when you get to the point of lowering the shafts to the ground (if that is where they are supposed to go), do lower them carefully. Dropping them with a sigh of relief will not do them any good at all. And the noise will give the horse a tremendous fright.

## Trace harness

A trace horse goes in front of a shaft horse to help him pull a heavy load, or to help him up a hill. This is called going tandem, an expression invented by some joker with a classical education, for the Latin word means 'at length', but only in the sense 'at last'.

The harness is sometimes called 'long gears' and occasionally 'string harness', which seems silly until you realise it describes a shape (the horses are strung out), not a material.

A trace-harness spreader. Notice the spreader-straps

No saddle or breeching is required. In addition to collar and hames and bridle, a trace horse needs the following:

(a) a crupper – a true crupper, because it goes from the collar right to the tail, a loop going round the horse's dock;

(b) a leather back-band, kept in position by the crupper, to hold the traces up;

(c) hip-straps, also supporting the traces, from the crupper down each side of the horse;

(d) the traces, running from the hame-hooks to staples on the underside (or sometimes the outside) of the front of the shafts. The crooks should be pushed upwards into the staples, not downwards – they are less likely to become undone that way. (The traces should not be called chains, even though that is what they are: otherwise, confusion arises with plough harness.)

(e) a spreader – a wooden or iron bar (normally a permanent fixture) between the traces behind the horse, wide enough to prevent them rubbing against his sides as he pulls and to enable each trace to continue in a straight line to its shaft;

(f) spreader-straps which run from the 'D' at each side of the spreader to meet at another D-hook on the crupper. These hold the spreader up behind the horse's back-side when he stops moving, but rise up slackly away from his quarters when he is pulling;

(g) a belly-band attached to the traces, to prevent them from pulling the collar up against the horse's wind-pipe.

When hooking on the trace horse, do the off-side trace first, in case the horse moves. It will save you walking all round the front to get to the off side or climbing over a fixed trace, catching your toe in it and measuring your length on the ground.

The faster horse, the 'goer' (who is probably the lighter of the two), should be the trace horse. With a powerful lumbering type in front and a weaker eager beaver behind, all three of you will be in difficulties, and spectators will have something worth watching.

If you are walking, you will go beside the head of the shaft horse. A short leading rein coming out horizontally over the top of the trace will be needed.

If you are driving, the reins of the trace horse should go through the rings on his own hames and then through two rein-guides fitted on the headpiece of the bridle of the shaft horse, which otherwise might get his head over them. Learn by steps. Try 'driving' from the

Hooking up the slack in traces. This is the safe way to get rid of unwanted chain

ground first, without a vehicle. When you put them to a vehicle, get a friend to drive the shaft horse while you drive the trace horse. After you have mastered that, attempt both at once.

To put a third horse in line, you crook the back end of his traces into the middle horse's traces a few inches behind his collar. But you will not need to reach these heights yet awhile.

If you have a cow in a ditch, you can get her out by putting a chain round her, connecting the ends to the spreader. Motor-bikes and old sofas can likewise be removed.

### Plough (and pole) harness

Any farm implement which does not have shafts requires only simple plough harness, either for a single horse or for two horses abreast, as in ploughing. This is 'going in chains'. In the Midlands it is sometimes known as 'G O gears' – 'Gee oh' meaning 'turn to the right', which is the most frequent instruction in ploughing.

Plough harness is lighter and less elaborate than trace harness, and the chains pull at an angle – the horse's neck being higher than the plough. In addition to bridle and collar and hames, you will need the following (for two horses):

(a) a coupling, between 20 and 25in long, of rope or chain or an adjustable strap, running between the inside bit-rings of the horses. This keeps them parallel to each other;

(b) the chains, hooked on to the hames and passing along the sides of each horse on a downward slope (be sure they are of the same length);

(c) a back-band, or plough-band, to support the chains;

(d) a crupper, similar to the trace-harness crupper. This is not for keeping the back-band down, because the angle of the chains does this. But, since the crupper holds back the collar, the horse without one can put his head down and eat, which is potentially dangerous. To do so, he might take an unexpected step forward, and you will find yourself on the ground;

(e) a set of whipple-trees or swingle-trees. The ends of the traces of each horse are hooked to the ends of a wooden or iron draught-bar. The middles of the two draught-bars are hooked to a weigh-tree, and the centre of the weigh-tree is hooked to the plough or other implement. (Alternatively, the two inside traces can be crossed over, so that

This is basic plough-harness. By running each line through the drop-link on the trace, you obtain a more direct communication between horse and man

each horse is exerting half his pull on both draught-bars.) The weigh-tree is one or two inches longer than the two bars in front of it.

Between one part of the country and another, there is more confusion in the words used for this contraption than for any other thing connected with the working of a horse. There ought to be one word for the bars on which the horses directly pull and another for the slightly longer one behind them. In a few districts there are, but in most there are not. Consequently, swingle-tree (swing-tree) whipple-tree (whippens), bodkins (badekins, battekins), and many other terms might refer to the whole of the apparatus, or to just one part of it. Words used for the rear bar include various forms of beam, baulk or bolt.

(f) tie-backs, to keep the horses working together. A tie-back is a light chain about 22 or 23in long, which runs from one horse's inside bit-ring, and is clipped with a spring hook to the other horse's trace, anything from three to seven or eight links back. Where you clip each tie-back depends on which horse needs tying back the most. You might in fact need only one. You can use a strap with buckles, but this might be awkward or impossible to thread through the trace.

If a horse is working really hard, the less leather in contact with his body the better, because he will sweat less. So in field work some people do without a back-band and even without a crupper. But the less experienced you are, the safer it is not to try to dispense with anything. In contrast, trace harness is often used at ploughing matches, simply because it gives more scope for decoration.

Only two lines are required. One is tied to the near-side bit-ring of the near-side horse and the other to the off-side bit-ring of the off-side horse. (When actually ploughing, the near-side horse is called the land horse and the other the furrow horse, because those are the places on which each walks.) The lines may be run through a ring suspended from the crupper by a short cord. It is essential to make sure they are of the right length.

To put two horses to a plough or any other implement, back them into position and fasten them together with the coupling; next fasten the two inner chains to the whipple-trees, and then the outer ones; finally adjust your tie-backs.

A form of plough harness is also used in two-horse waggons which have a central pole. (Some such waggons have double shafts, not a pole, and then each horse obviously wears shaft harness.) For

The tie-backs are well shown in this picture of two horses ploughing

A pair of Thwaites' black Shire geldings, at the Blackburn brewery, display their pole harness to good effect (*David Kay*)

agricultural use, the only additions are a neck-yoke or coupling and two pole-straps or collar-straps to hold the pole up. With commercial vehicles, you require proper pole traces, breechings (lighter than required in shaft harness, because the collar takes the weight, with chains going from the breech-band to the hame-hook), a lightweight saddle or pad (there is no weight on the horses' backs), and pair-horse reins.

The horses should be backed into place, with the pole lying on the ground between them. A second man should be there to hold them. After they are coupled, the pole-straps should be done up first, and the traces afterwards. This is very important because, in the event of the horses running away, the most appalling accident would occur if they were attached to the vehicle while the pole was still on the ground. For the same reason, when shutting out you must undo the traces before releasing the horses from the pole. It is obviously important also to make sure that the traces are exactly the right length.

## Show harness and decoration

Why decorate your horse's harness? This is a silly question. Why not attend a dinner in your gardening clothes? In the dim past, decorations arose from various superstitions, too, such as averting the evil eye by means of harness brasses, and so on. But that has nothing to do with us. We are just talking about dressing up.

You can have a special set of show harness – your horse's 'Sunday best'. That is fine. You can even get expensive patent leather, but it would be a waste of money. This is only for town display, and at some shows it is not allowed even in the commercial classes. It is certainly not right for agricultural classes at any time.

In those areas where they are fussy about their traditions (and they happen to be those where most of the best horses are still bred), chrome or other labour-saving plated chains are definitely not the thing. They bring a sneer to the lips of all. Only burnished ones are tolerated at shows. They are terribly hard to keep clean and rust with amazing rapidity, almost as soon as you breathe on them. You may think that wilfully to have and to clean such things is a form of masochism. But it does not matter what you think. A Guardsman would be happier in an old sweater and jeans. But he does not mention this to the sergeant major on parade.

If a horse appears in a harness class or turn-out class, you are permitted, indeed expected, to add entirely non-functional items to his harness. Small brass studs can be put on all narrow straps, and as borders on broad ones. All broad straps can have brasses, but you should see to it that the ones you use are all of the same basic shape – all oval, all square, or all triangular. The saddler will put them on for you. Similarly, all buckles (brass-mounted, please) should be matching, throughout the set – the same pattern for little ones as for big.

Extra leather, whose sole purpose is to carry more brasses, can include, perhaps first and foremost, a breast-strap, often loosely referred to as a 'martingale', because it runs from the bottom of the collar between the horse's legs to the girth-strap. But it is not there to hold the horse's head down, like a real martingale. In fact, it really is very loose. The correct number of brasses to put on this is five.

Among other leather items you can use are side-straps, hanging down each side in front of the loin straps; a leading-rein, which can be held up by a rein hanger from the meeter-strap; a hame-strap, running between the crooks of the hames; and, on the bridle, a face piece hanging from the brow-band, and neck-straps from the top of the head-strap of the bridle to the bearing-rein. Perhaps we ought to stop there, though we have not exhausted the catalogue of what you might encounter and, with apologies, we have ignored Scottish custom in the interest of simplicity.

Finally among leather items, the housen (or cape, cap, fan, hood, knub or any one of a dozen names) originally had a practical purpose. It is a piece of stiffened leather standing upright behind the hames.

A farm gelding in show harness. How much or how little you add to normal working harness is a matter of personal choice (*Edward Clapham*)

These two horses are wearing full Cornish decorated harness (*Gordon Adlam*)

During a storm of rain, it was dropped so as to lie flat on the horse between his collar and saddle: it was raised again afterwards to prevent the horse becoming intolerably hot. This horse-umbrella, of various shapes, grew to ridiculous proportions in some areas a couple of centuries or so ago – big enough to look, when upright, like a sort of sail, as if to send the wearer scudding and skimming across country. Nowadays, a housen is small, decorative and non-functional.

To complete our tally of ornaments, fly head terrets, usually in the form of a brass disc screwed into a fitting on the top of the head-strap, and sets of brushes and bells can here have only a mention. We must avoid the danger of entering into the esoteric realm of 'decorated' harness. The use of plumes, flowers, tassels, fringes and so on is not only a specialist but a regional art. What the artists do in Cornwall is different from what is done in Lancashire, which is different again from Scotland. Indeed, our best advice to the beginner is to be restrained, at least to start with, even in the use of such things as breast-straps and other leather. It is better to have only a little that is good than a lot of rubbishy stuff eccentrically festooning the horse, like old-fashioned Christmas decorations. The plaiting of manes and tails is of course another form of decoration. A word about that later.

## The care of harness

There is a famous short story about a man who tried to cure his golfing faults with thick elastic bands placed round his body and limbs. Eventually there were so many that he was completely trussed up. When one snapped, the stress upon the others set off a series of reactions during which he was strangely and grotesquely distorted. Horse-harness, though it may seem just as complicated at first, is essentially logical, though we can learn one lesson from the story. That is, it must fit correctly and be adjusted correctly at all points if the horse is to be both efficient and comfortable.

You need spare collars – what if one is away for repair? For all items you should have duplicate bits and pieces. If you are in the middle of a job, you cannot wait for the saddler. However, if everything is of good quality (brass buckles, for example, and not tin ones, which get stuck with rust and age) and if you look after it well (store it carefully), it is amazing how long harness will last. It will out-live you, and your son, and all your children's children.

Oil all leather, including head-collars, at least twice a year on the outside with neat's-foot oil, and on the inside once a year. For shows, clean with good leather polish. Take special care to brush and dry the inside of collars and saddles, to prevent them getting lumpy and hard. It will take you all day to clean harness properly for a show, but it is a most rewarding task.

# 7
# Breaking and Training

In the interest of clarity and simplicity, we write as though you have bought a young horse and are going to break him yourself. In fact, if you are wise, your first horse will be a mature one. But you will still need to know whether he has properly learned to perform the tasks you hope he will do, and you can assess the completeness of his education only if you understand what that has comprised. Furthermore, your horse is not the only one of you that ought to be well trained.

## Yourself

Safety is a recurrent theme in this book, and here we deal with one or two points to be thought of at all times, whether your horse is sensible and well trained or badly trained and giddy. They are basic to your own discipline.

When leading a horse, keep your feet out of the way, especially when turning him sideways. His foot will come out farther than you think. Never put your foot where he is going to put his.

If you are uncertain of him, or if he is not fully broken, never get yourself into a position where the reins are too far away to grab. Never leave your horse facing an open gate, while you go back to fetch your coat at the bottom of the field. He may decide to go home on his own – and demolish the first gatepost, or the second, in addition to the cart, or whatever else is with him. Do not, as a kindly thought, remove the bridle while you take a rest or have something to eat or drink. He will assume he is now free, and will take off.

Never stand close to a shaft which is pointing at you. If for some reason the horse jumps forward, a hole will be driven through you, unless you are a midget, in which case you will be scalped or decapitated.

Never get into a cart by standing on the spoke of a wheel. A sudden movement by the horse at that moment can produce a wide variety of

131

How not to get into a cart. What will happen if the horse moves?

results, all painful, many complicated and some horrific. Never ride sitting on a shaft. It is illegal on the road, though many modern policemen may not know. But we are concerned not so much with your observing the law as with a loss to the ranks of budding horsemen, should you fall off. An iron-tyred wheel tends to slice the body in two. In fact, never ride on anything that is not meant to be ridden on. That includes every implement. In an emergency, you cannot

The correct way to get into a cart. If the horse moves now, the young lady can swing herself on - and she is also holding the reins

jump to right or left because it is too wide, or backwards because of the working machinery, or forwards because of the horses.

Never work two young horses together, unless you have plenty of experienced help. One might start off on some madness, the other will not have the sense or experience to restrain him, and both will make each other worse in a crisis.

Harness must be in good order. If something breaks, even an old horse will take fright; on a young horse, faulty harness is a time bomb. The same applies to chains and in particular to shafts. If one snaps, all sorts of things can happen – including the horse getting poked in the guts by the broken end. Furthermore, if a partly-trained horse discovers that something disintegrates when he kicks it, he will try to kick his way out of everything. Whatever you spend on all these things, it is money well spent.

### First steps

Real breaking and training ought to begin in the autumn when the horse is two. By then, he should already have been taught to lead and to have his legs picked up. He ought to be used to being handled and should have a quiet disposition. He should also take it calmly if he is tied up. If not, teach him at once, with an extremely strong rope halter tied to an immovable object. When he realises that he cannot bring the whole building down, he will learn to stand. But if you are silly enough, after tying him up for the first time, to leave him while you use the telephone, he might break his neck in the sheer terror of his efforts to get free.

Next, put a head collar on him and attach a breaking bit to it. Leave him in the loose box for an hour or two. Then lead him about. Put some harness on him. He should learn to stand still while it is put on and taken off. Lead him round with it on, so that he becomes accustomed to the feel of it as he moves.

The next stage is to get someone to help you – a reasonably agile sort of fellow. If your Trusty Adviser is now a bit slow or shaky on his pins, he would not be the right man for this humble but vital job. You want to keep him alive and healthy as long as you can. Your assistant in what is to follow should love you as a brother, since he must stay with you until the end even if he gets bruised and bloody.

Breaking harness, with a mouthing bit. In this, a horse learns his basic commands – *whoa, come here, wook off* and *walk on*, or whatever language is spoken in your area

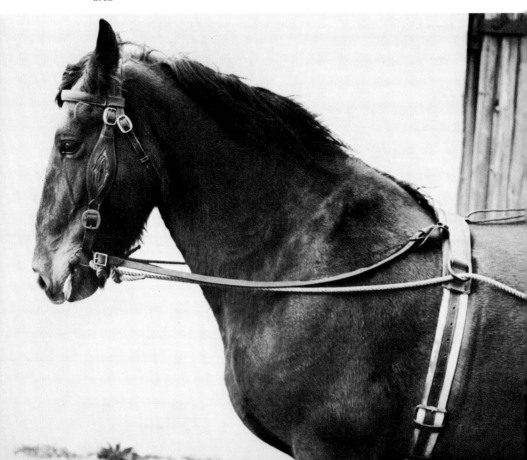

Put a good halter on the horse, with a long rope. Your helper is going to hold this, and it should be of sufficient length so that he can jump out of the way without letting go. You now put a bridle on and attach lines, and start teaching your horse to be driven. You are aiming to get him walking about nicely, doing as he is told – told by you. Your helper says nothing whatever, at any time, and should try to avoid even swearing under his breath. He is there only for emergencies, to pull the horse round if he starts to go. Otherwise he does nothing, except hold the rope. Your horse is learning to be driven, not led. If your assistant speaks to him, he will think he is being led, and there is no lesson at all.

Say nothing yourself, either to your horse or to anyone else, while he is at his lessons, apart from your commands, which must be short, sharp and clear. Do not expect him to pick out your instructions from the middle of a complex sentence. Use his name, though. In a well-trained team, none should move until he hears his own name spoken. The only other words permissible are sounds rather than words, used sparingly to denote praise and approval, or sharp rebuke.

Words of command vary from region to region – *whoa*; *walk on*; *come here*; *walk back* etc. Whatever vocabulary you use, give him as few words as possible to learn but make sure he masters them well. Gradually teach him to turn which way you require by word of mouth, to stop, to start and stop, and to back. Do this every day, perhaps a three-quarter hour lesson each time.

Make him walk through puddles. Some horses will try to go round them. When drawing a cart through a gateway, to do this would cause problems. Make him even walk through a stream. You probably will not come across a ford when you are out, but you might. Put plastic fertiliser bags around the yard, and paper sacks. Chuck them about, or anything else you can think of. Make him walk over them. Some will make a crackling noise, and some will seem to fly up in the air if he scuffs them. All these things are good experience for him.

Get him to pass tractors and cars, to realise that they will not rear up or bite him. Show him the milk tanker, and see what he thinks of that. Start the tractor up some distance away. Provided that this does not worry him, start it up fairly close to him.

Change the harness from cart gear to plough harness, and then to trace harness, so that he becomes used to the different sorts. Do not use your best harness. He might not do it any good if he plunges about. But it must be serviceable stuff which will not break. A fright at this stage will be more than a temporary set-back. Next put some traces on him, so that when he turns he can feel the chains on his leg. Let him step over the chains, then step back. Attach some sort of log – a railway sleeper is ideal. Your helper at his head is really necessary now, for this is the first time the horse has experienced the effort of pulling anything. Lessons of 20 min or 1/2 hr duration are enough.

When he is perfect at this, and does not mind the chains wrapping up round his legs, put him to a small harrow and do the exercise with that. Chain harrows make a noise, and there will be a different feel on his shoulders. Go on at this exercise daily until he is perfect. He might be all right two days but on the third have a funny turn, so always have your assistant with you.

If he does take off because something has alarmed him, there is danger. If he is allowed to go straight, he will go faster and faster and nothing will stop him. He will get more and more frightened. So let go of the off-side rein. This, and your friend at his head, will pull him round near-sided. You may seem to be going at a rate of knots, but it will be in diminishing circles. Eventually there is nothing for your horse to do but stop. He certainly will not have got away with you, or without you. Your helper will feel a hero, and will expect a glass of something rewarding. But not yet.

When a halt has been achieved, disentangle everything and start the practice all over again, as if nothing had happened. At once. On no account retire at this stage. And do not chastise your horse. He was frightened by something. No one had warned him that you were going to sneeze.

Next, put him with an old quiet horse if you have one. If you have bred him, his mother will do admirably. Still with your helper at his head, put them together in a chain harrow – not a double-spiked one; a single-sided harrow is safer. Your assistant can encourage him when he flags, and his companion will pull him along anyway, or help pull him back to a sensible pace, as the case may be. He will probably get in a muck sweat but do not worry about that if he seems to be going along all right. If you have no old horse, you have just *got* to hold him all the time, to a steady pace.

When in pairs, novice horses find turning difficult to learn at first. They have to grasp that it is necessary to go faster, or slower, than the other horse. A young one teamed with a quiet old one will go faster because he has to, and is pushed round if turning the other way. You will by now have a fair idea of how well he is going to do. Even if you are disappointed, do not forget that whenever he does something right you must praise him.

136

A young horse's first load should be a log, or something similar – just heavy enough to keep the traces taut. Notice the helper, walking well behind his shoulder and with a line to his head. She is there only for emergencies

A little bit of actual work can follow, but not too much; a couple of hours at the most. Some people break horses in on the plough. If you do that, put him in the furrow, where he will learn what it is all about. Horses trained like this can become good plough horses for the rest of their lives. But, though it is good breaking, you cannot afford to plough a field just to train a horse.

Do not reward him for the tiny bit of work he has done by suddenly feeding him a lot of high-energy food like oats and beans. This will make him flighty and excitable, and you will lose the battle. And if you are yourself excitable and flighty, every lesson will make him worse than he was before. A man who is always in a hurry should not be training animals. And one who is quick-tempered will start by upsetting his horse and end by making the animal as volatile as himself. You need patience, time and an even temper. What he learns at this stage, a horse never forgets.

Backing is more unnatural for him than for us. So, to get him used to what is involved in backing into shafts, place two pieces of wood as in our picture, and reverse him between them. If he smashes one, it is less expensive than a real shaft. But leave actual shaft-work training until he is three – the following spring.

## Shaft work

When you start, put him in any cart – not a waggon. It is best to do this exercise in a small paddock. A lesson in the yard would be dangerous and expensive if it is full of Rolls-Royces.

Have help at his head, again – you do not want him careering off. When you get into the cart yourself, your horse might be able to see you over his blinkers if they are not well fitted. If he does happen to catch a glimpse of you, it will be a nasty shock. Why have you suddenly grown twelve feet tall? A horse can become very alarmed at someone suddenly looming up over him.

After a while, put something in the cart to make it heavier, and with a different balance. But not too much. If it is too heavy, you will make him a jibber for life. He also has to learn that he must push the shaft round in turning. Teach him to back the cart. Some take to this better than others. If he is a bit shy about it, try backing him down a very gentle slope – enough to make the cart require very little pressure, but not enough to pull him backwards at ten miles an hour.

The time will inevitably come when you think you can risk a lesson without your helper. Only at the end of it will you know if your faith is justified. But there are one or two special precautions you can take. If you have to stop to open a gate, you should have a long line on your horse so that you never let go of him. One free step is quickly followed by another, and before you have abandoned the gate he will be in a canter, and you will never catch him, even if you are a fairish runner. If you want to stop to put some bales on the cart or to take them off, tie him with his halter to something immovable. This will teach him to stand.

If you have a double-shafted waggon, put him in that with the old horse. He can go only where his companion goes, and at his companion's speed. He might rear or jump up, but will soon be restrained. And, if he is disinclined to go as he should, the old horse will take and make him. Then try him in succession at anything which has shafts – say, a roller. The sound of iron wheels is frightening if he is not used to them. So try him with those. Try him on every surface you

This horse is learning to back into shafts. Look where he has put his foot! If it were a real shaft, he would not be doing it much good

possess – particularly tarmac. The public roads are not the best place to meet this for the first time.

Never let him have his own way. If you do, he will try it on again. What you set out to do in one training session, try to achieve – without forcing, and with endless patience. Finish one exercise before you go on to the next. Do not be over-ambitious. If he will not go, even after one good smack, it is no good beating him. There is something wrong somewhere. Find out what it is.

If your horse does run away, you will have to decide when to abandon ship. When horses run away, they are like a boy running away from school: they run home. The difference is that, cluttered up with a cart, the horse may never reach his home in one piece. But if they are terrified, they lose their wits and run anywhere. Do you want everything smashed up, including yourself? Even a thick thorn hedge that you cannot see through will not necessarily stop him if he is in full flight. You must not jump out immediately, for the worst thing you can do is to let the horse get away. One such escapade might spoil him for life. And if your horse and you and the cart are hurtling towards old Mr and Mrs Scrubbins, both stone deaf, who are looking for mushrooms, you must remain in your vehicle longer than would otherwise be sensible.

After such an incident, provided that all is intact, including the Scrubbins, sort things out straight away, and immediately begin the exercise all over again. To pack up for the day would be as bad for your own morale as for your horse. If you have had a real scare, you might never bring yourself to have another go unless you do so on the spot. Try to puzzle out what was the prime cause of the trouble.

After a few frights and many disappointments, you might come to the conclusion that your horse is just no damn' good at all. You might be right. There are some that are hare-brained, but not many. Before definitely deciding, pause to think whether the deficiency is not his, but yours, and whether, though difficult, he would have done better in more experienced hands. If this is a possibility, admit defeat and hand him over to someone else to break. If your Trusty Adviser reluctantly tells you it is not your fault, then the only answer is sale (and be honest about what you are selling) or slaughter.

On the other hand, you may find you have got hold of a slow-witted horse. These, in the long run, can be almost as dangerous as the mad ones, for they will not do the sensible thing even when they are old and experienced.

As long as you are training a horse, whether he is sensible and intelligent, or dull, or excitable, the golden rule is 'little and often' – for all of them. And 'often' means daily. Week-ends alone are no earthly good. If you keep re-starting, you will get nowhere. And your horse is getting older every week.

The biggest enemy we face today in a job like this is time, or the lack of it. In the old days, the services of skilled horsemen were so cheap, and they worked so long, that they could be given time to train a horse at the horse's speed. But we cannot change the horse's tempo because times are different. If we want a horse to respond, we must *somehow* adapt to his pace.

Your farm work or your business must not suffer in favour of the horse. You might therefore have to pay for him to be broken. This would be a pity, because you will miss a lot of fun. But, if you do have to delegate, get someone who really knows his job and who will be as kind and patient as he is firm. But, should you tackle the job yourself, do not let other people mess around with him until he is fully trained. You must do it all yourself. And do not allow an audience while the lessons are in progress.

If your horse is normally intelligent, you can break him in a few weeks. But it will take him twelve months really to learn properly – to be experienced enough to become 'anybody's horse', as he should be. In that time he will have lived and practised through every season of the year. This is important. Even more important, however, is regular and prolonged practice.

So keep on with your revision lessons, but do not give him any hard work until he has reached the age of at least three-plus. And do not try to be amibitious – to teach him to trot in a cart when he is young. He needs to learn to be steady first. You can always make him go faster by giving him a bit of corn. But it is a hell of a job to make him go slower. Say you meet someone at the bottom of your drive, and stop for a chat. If your horse can go safely back on his own, and be waiting for you at the stable-door, you have produced a useful horse. Well done!

What if you have no work for him to do? Is it really necessary to go through all this training? Yes, of course. What *are* you going to do with him? Will you never want to take him to a show? Never appear in public? Will you never be forced to sell him? Of what value is a cart-horse if he is useless? Less than none, because an untrained domestic animal, of such a size and weight as he is, is a liability.

## On the road

Whether you are keen to take your horse out on the public highway or terrified at the thought, you should do so. But not before he is quiet and completely under your control in every novel circumstance that you have been able to fabricate at home. The dangers of taking him to a show, though different, are more numerous. So, unless you propose to keep him in private at home all his life, road work is the only feasible intermediary stage between practising within your gates and performing in public. In any case, something may crop up in the course of daily life which makes a journey along the road essential.

For your first trip, take what precautions you can. Do not set off along that narrow winding road with tall hedges on each side at o8.43 if the school bus, driven by that chap who is always a bit late, comes in the opposite direction at o8.45. Do not take him under a railway bridge when the Inter-City is due, if you are not certain whether he likes trains. Even though he may, he will not associate a sudden deafening pandemonium a few feet over his head with what he has learned about the operations of British Rail.

He will probably have got used to a bird suddenly flying out of a hedge in front of his nose. But idiots on motor-bikes who come up behind you and pass as close as they dare, revving up, are worse. Perhaps such morons are not found in your district. But the species is migratory, and a Sunday afternoon in summer might bring a flock of specimens. So choose your time carefully.

You have to try to get inside the horse's brain if you are really going to think ahead for all possible danger-spots. He might be suspicious of a couple of dustbins outside that gate. He might not like that creaking sign-board. Look out for such things as these. Thanks to your training, he will superciliously ignore the odd plastic bag lying in his path. But he may be appalled by a zebra crossing, and you will feel ridiculous if he will not cross over it, or tries to put his feet only on the black parts. If he meets big white arrows, he will not try to follow them, but he might halt and snort. At a box junction, he might stop completely, or try to play hopscotch. One man went so far as to paint a zebra crossing on his drive in order to overcome that kind of problem.

Gradually, or quite soon, he will calmly ignore even such unpredictable surprises as the dog which suddenly rushes down its garden path barking furiously as you pass. And you yourself will gain confidence in your new sort of road sense. You might begin to fancy that

Teaching a horse to meet all eventualities on the road. After a few times, all the engines will be running. When he accepts that, they will be brought closer together so that he has only a narrow gap to walk through

you, too, could train those brewery horses which go about their lawful business so splendidly amid the uproar of the city streets – or even the police horses which are shock-proof on lawless occasions. That is fine, but do not relax. The next barking dog might cause your horse to step slightly sideways. Young Alfie, not trained by you the great expert, will come off his bike, and you will come down a peg.

Try to make it an unfailing rule to thank car-drivers who give way to you, or who slow down or show any other consideration. In this respect, horse-people do not always have a good reputation. In our cars, we have all met people on horseback riding abreast, who return a minor courtesy with an icy stare. This makes us fume until, the next time, we are rewarded with a brilliant smile. We should all do everything possible to give the heavy-horse fraternity a fair name. However there is no need to overdo things. One horseman was noted for the dashing manner in which he swept his hat off and extravagantly bowed to those he judged to have been considerate. One day, he was so busy doing this that he toppled his cart, his horse and himself into a ditch.

143

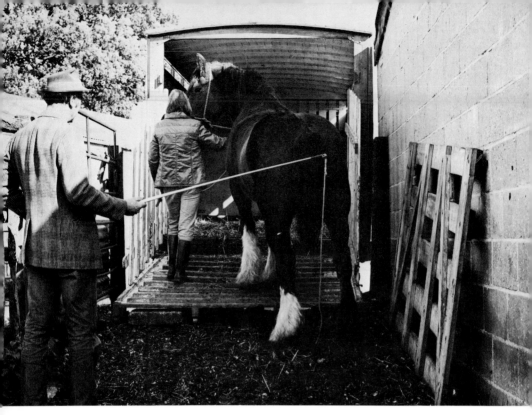

Gentle persuasion! Notice the narrow pen, and the very slight incline of the ramp

## Loading up for a journey

The horse which walks jauntily to the tailboard and goes up every time, as good as gold, is a joy. But nothing is more frustrating than the one which refuses. There are two possible reasons for refusing. Either he is frightened, or he is being awkward.

The horse that will not load from the beginning is less likely to be bloody-minded than afraid. Try to overcome this fear in private. A good method is to make a concrete ramp over which, when your lorry is backed right up to it, the tailboard can exactly fit. Build the side up into walls, and you will have no problem. But make certain he really is confident by getting him to go up without hesitation several days in succession away from the ramp, before you start any journeys.

If he normally loads without trouble, but then suddenly refuses, the reason might be cussedness. He would rather stay at home today. Or he is at a show and would prefer to remain a bit longer. However, it might be some new fear that you do not understand. Beating a frightened horse is useless: he only gets worse. So do not whack him

He is now so used to being loaded up that he seems to be looking forward to a day out

until you have thought it out. You must establish the cause before you can find the remedy. He might have had a bad journey the day before. Or it might be a little thing, such as the back wheels of the lorry being on a hump and the tailboard therefore too steep for him to be happy about. The remedy, too, might be as simple. If you are loading two horses, put the other one in first and give him something to eat. His recalcitrant companion may then unhesitatingly follow.

At a show, you are never more likely to collect a group of spectators than when your horse will not load. Some will proffer advice, as conflicting as it is useless. The others will just enjoy the free entertainment. Keep your temper. Your duty is to the horse, not to the audience, which hopes you will go raving mad. You might be able to persuade two kind people to draw up a lorry on each side of yours. Then, if your horse is going at all, he can only go one way, and that is up and in.

Should all fail, a sense of loneliness may steal over you as the showground empties and even the loafers drift away because their spouses are calling. But cheer up. Perhaps after an interval of peace during which you yourself calm down (this could be an important factor) your horse will suddenly load up as calmly and sweetly as if there had never been any fuss. Or possibly some Samaritan, a more experienced horseman with a sharper eye and a bit of that sixth sense that grows with the years, will help you to do the trick. He was not in the original knot of spectators. He appears as if from nowhere, says little, takes over, and then goes away again. On the way home, you will have time to puzzle out your new experience in horse psychology.

# 8

# Your Horse on Parade

For many, this chapter may be the climax of the book. You buy a horse, you feed and bed and groom him: you make him happy, you keep him fit: you give him harness to wear, even a cart or waggon or implements to pull. But the visionary gleam in your eye comes from the thought in your head that, even if he is not the finest specimen of a cart-horse in all Britain, he might be able to beat a couple of others at next year's Lower Muddington Show.

### Plaiting up

At a show or on any occasion that you bring your horse before the public, you will have to plait him up at both ends. Decoration has always been the sole reason for doing the mane. Plaiting the tail is practical as well, to prevent it from getting over the reins or in the traces or from becoming filthy in muddy conditions; but here we are concerned only with adornment.

Unfortunately you cannot learn this art from a book. We could have a good try to take you through the motions, but it is so much more sensible to get someone to teach you that we deliberately leave it to your Trusty Adviser. In any case, there are several ways of doing the tail, largely dependent on regional ideas and the breed of horse. And the mane may be either completely plaited along the top of the neck, or only half done, one side of it being neatly combed downwards.

Have your first lesson in autumn or winter, long before the show season starts. Remember that you have only your poor horse to practise on and also that you need to become reliably proficient. There is no time on the show-ground to bodge up several embarrassing efforts before you get it right.

First choose your colour(s), two or just one. To be effective, they must be bright and your choice is therefore from red, blue, green, yellow and white. Turquoise and salmon pink would scarcely do.

(*above*) Start plaiting as close behind the ears as possible. The horse's head must be kept absolutely still; (*below left*) The flights should be plaited in with the bass, not twisted round it afterwards; (*below right*) For a horse to be shown in harness, carry on plaiting to just in front of his collar, but continue farther on a horse to be shown in hand. The plait must be kept tight all the time

Some colours look particularly well on certain coats. One famous brewery uses only white; all their horses are blacks, and this makes a marvellous contrast. But, in your case, whereas you will want to retain your colours, the second horse you buy might be quite different from the first.

Rye straw, which once was used, is almost impossible to get and most people use bass (bast), which the handicraft people call raffia. Buy it in hanks, not little packets. Split each strand down so that you have strips of the same width. Then you can dye it in the colours of your choice. Before plaiting, put the required amount in water to soak. It will dry hard on mane and tail. You can use wool, which of course can be bought ready dyed. But it is spongy and difficult to plait firm and tight.

You will also need flights for the mane. These should be plaited into the bass, one for every other plait, as you work – not just poked in afterwards. Their number will be fewer if the horse is wearing a collar and harness, because less of the mane is then visible. Electric flex is quite good for the stem of a flight. It is strong enough to stand up and yet pliable enough for the job. For the actual flights, do not use plastic flowers. They look ridiculous, and in any case you do not want a shower of them all over the place if your horse happens to shake his head. Use ribbons of the same colours.

The aim of plaiting a mane is not only to make a neat job but to improve the outline of the neck. An expert at this art can make even a very poor neck look impressive, especially if he has craftily put a little roll of straw covered with cloth in the parting of the mane and plaited round it in such a way that the judge does not see. The flights also help to carry the eye of the beholder upward, to give the impression of a good big neck.

Once the mane is done up with bass, do not let the horse put his head down below his knees. Hold it up and, if he has to be tied, tie it up high. Otherwise, and if the raffia is really tight, it will be agony for him. If he puts his head right down suddenly, it might even scalp him. It will not hurt if the bass is loose: but that is bad plaiting.

As for the tail, whether you plait the top and leave the rest loose or plait it all up, you use a tail ring or standards. You can either make a tail ring or buy a specially made one of plastic-covered wire. It must stand well up to the top of the horse's quarters, to make a level line for the eye. If you shave the dock, plaiting is easier. But recently there has been some agitation against this practice.

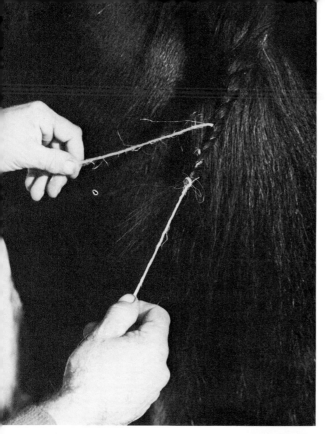

Start plaiting as high up the tail as you can. Just before the end of your plait, thread some thin string through, and tie off. Put the plait up and over, and through the back. Wrap round and tie, to make a bun

Tie on your tail-loop and cover with ribbon

## Advance preparations

Until you have taken your horse to a show, you do not really know how he will respond. Crowds of people are a novelty. *En masse*, round the ring, they are one thing. Wandering round the ground, they are another. Even sensible people, on holiday, can behave like half-wits. A mother bumps a pram into the back leg of your stationary horse. Will he smash it to smithereens? Father thrusts a toddler into his face. A tiny child stands underneath him or plays with his foot. Where have the parents gone? They will re-appear if their infant is kicked high in the air.

There are new noises. Perhaps a brass band, organs, steam engines, even a fun-fair. There will certainly be loud-speakers. The ripple of applause round a ring-side sounds very different from the crackle from a grand-stand or indoors. And what a lot of other horses there are! How exciting!

Do not take him until you are confident that he will be all right. If he is not, he will at best make you look silly and, at worst, create danger. If something causes him to 'take off', you will not be able to abandon ship and resort to silent prayer. The chain reaction among the other horses is too appalling to contemplate. Fatalities at shows are rare, and should not happen when well-trained horses are under the control of good men. But recently there have been many dangerous situations caused by inexperienced and foolish newcomers. Do not be the first to make the front-page headline.

What can you do at home to prepare your horse? Practise him walking round the edge of a field. Not slouching, but stepping out well. Practise walking forty or fifty yards in a dead straight line. Turn, and come back to where you started. Turn again and trot the same distance, and come back again. When you say 'walk', he walks: and when you say 'trot', he moves immediately into an easy rhythm that enables you to get in step with him.

Your own action, especially at the trot, is important. Your right hand is holding the horse. The left does not flay about, but remains motionless. Your steps should measure the horse's, in time with his front feet. Your body and head travel horizontally, without other movement. You may be surprised that you have to bring your knees up very high.

Get members of your family to criticise. They may say your belly wobbles or that your little legs go like pistons. However, the judge will not be looking at you, and the horse will not go right unless you do. If you are so funny as your family claims, you will have to get used to ribaldry from strangers.

Practise your horse stepping back a pace or two in a collected and orderly way. You may have to do this several times in the ring. Teach him to stand well. He must be 'on his legs' – all four, not resting one. And straight, not stretched out like a hackney.

If you like, go into the highways and byways and get as many people as possible to come into the field and create a mild uproar while you go through your exercises. Do anything that you can think of to simulate what will actually happen.

Teach your horse to go well on any surface – concrete, tarmac, gravel, dry grass, wet grass. One man took a horse to a top-class show and realised too late why it was at a loss. All its exercise had been on the roads, and he was asking it to perform on spongy soaking grass.

For turn-out classes, you can similarly practise what you will actually do in the ring. But for your first show, you will probably enter only the in-hand classes.

Try to have your horse in his finest condition on show day. The more experienced you become, the more you will appreciate the niceness of timing that this requires. The show animal has to be just a little on the plump side. Bursting with health, but not in hard training. He would require a couple of weeks to lean down into working condition – a gradual process if he were not to knock himself up. During that time he would lose some of his show glamour.

As for grooming, plan this beauty-process weeks before. We have dealt already with that. But two other questions must be answered before show day arrives. What are you going to wear? This depends to some extent on what classes you are going to show in, and so we cover this under those heads. And, in a harness class, do you appreciate what is meant by 'clean'? That, too, is best discussed later.

Finally, make certain that a friend will be able to come with you – someone prepared to fetch things, to stay with the horse while you go for a drink, to do anything to help. If your family is involved, make it plain to the junior members that you are not going to be such a fool as to let a boy or girl lead the horse around, or take him in the ring. They may be able to do anything you can do. But a sudden emergency and a startled horse would be unfair to your children or nephews and nieces. If they failed to deal with the crisis, your negligence would be criminal, morally if not in law.

## The day of the show

However long or short your journey, take all you will possibly need, for wet weather or dry – cleaning kit and decorations, food for humans and horse and, if in doubt, water for your horse. Not every field borrowed for a small event has water laid on, or you might have to walk a long way to get it. You will also need a fly-sheet. A mare you will show in an ordinary white halter, and the same applies to a foal. For a gelding, you will use an in-hand bridle. Compile a check-list. Few people have actually forgotten to load the horse, but Baby's food left in the kitchen can spoil your day out.

Get up early and give yourself plenty of time. You do not want to upset your horse. An animal's reaction to frantic or hysterical behaviour is never co-operative. Put out by the air of tension, he gets edgy and confused, and slows everything down. The day you oversleep will be the day he is awkward to box. When there is plenty of time to spare, he will walk up the ramp like a commuter boarding a train.

Consider how long it will take you to get to the showground, and add a good bit to it. You will probably find yourself with an hour to spare at the other end. But leave just fifteen minutes later, and you will get tangled up in the traffic and fume at the wheel.

A word about how you drive. Remember the horse is standing up. The motion of the lorry is as unpredictable as that of a tube train, and he has no hands. You can help him a lot by proceeding at a uniform speed as long as you can. He will quickly learn to understand that as soon as your foot comes off the accelerator, some change is imminent. He will brace himself against a stop, a bend or a swerve. It is marvellous how soon he will become an experienced traveller, if you are a good driver.

Horses do not like going very fast, and of course emergency action at high speed gives the horse little or no warning to brace his legs. Go steadily. This is bad luck on the driver behind who wants to pass. But he will have to wait a bit. If you find yourself going fast, get up earlier next time.

Allow ample time for plaiting up on arrival and any other necessary titivations. One of these could be to wipe your horse over with a *slightly* paraffined cloth. This gives a good shine and helps to keep flies off. But not too much. You do not want him reeking, or in danger of catching fire.

What about your own appearance? You really should not be in shirt sleeves, and no one will admire your braces. Do not wear wellies.

Boots are obviously better than shoes. Not only are they more comfortable during a long day on one's feet, but they do a little towards resisting the pressure should your horse accidentally stand where you have left your foot.

You have chosen to appear in a public competition in front of people who have all paid money to see it. You will also meet a judge who is the greatest expert that the show committee could persuade to come. He is paid nothing and the expenses he claims or is offered always leave him out of pocket, not to mention the loss of his time. Have a good look at him when at last you enter the ring. You will find little wrong with his turn-out. If he judged a big show the week before, he will look the same now as he did then. He is there only to judge your horse, not you. But you should pay him the compliment of appreciating his presence.

These observations may appear so superfluous as to be insulting. But dress and manners will probably be so much worse than they would have been at the same show fifty years ago, that you might get confused and imagine that braces, a dirty shirt, wellies and a cigarette are *de rigueur*. There are, of course, many owners who set as high a standard for themselves as for their horses, and, in this particular, 'silly Suffolk' should rather be re-named 'civil'.

There is such a thing, of course, as being over-dressed. At Lower Muddington Show with the worst horse in a weak class, you would look faintly absurd in faultless leggings, bespoke jacket and bowler hat. If you can afford to look like that, why not buy a decent horse?

On arrival, find out where you are to put your lorry. If there is any choice, you will be glad you arrived early, for you can pick a spot that might remain relatively peaceful. This is important at small shows where there are no boxes for the horses, because your site will be a temporary home for you, your family and the horse. Which way will the sun be shining? The wind? Will it pour with rain?

Collect your number from the secretary, if it has not been sent to you in advance. Find out if the classes are running to time. Discover whether there is a steward for the horse-lines, who will keep in touch with you and tell you what to do. If not, you will have to have an ear cocked for the public-address system. Vow to be watchful all day long that, win or lose, your horse does not kick another, or kick a member of the public. Offer a prayer that the public will enable you to keep your resolve.

Be in the collecting ring in plenty of time. The hassle of not being quite ready to come forward is agonising enough, but it is worse if

Warm water, a good animal shampoo and a water brush will get a leg clean. Rinse out with clean water. Walk or trot the horse on clean ground to shake out excess droplets

Stand the horse's foot on a split-open sack and rub wood flour well in until the leg is dry. When you arrive at the showground, brush and comb out what flour is still there

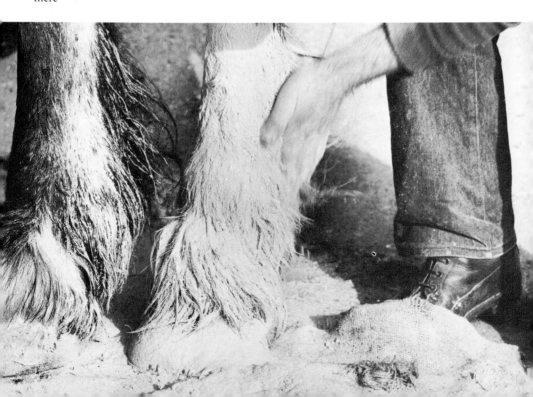

you incur the wrath of the officials. Throw away that cigarette. Your nerves will have to be controlled by your own will-power from now on.

There is no need to try to be first in the ring, but there is no point in being last. More important, remember that your entrance is the first time the judge sees your horse, and *the impression he forms will stick in his mind*. The contest *has already begun*. So get your horse walking as smartly as you and he know how. Make sure you do everything your class steward tells you to do. If his instructions turn out to be wrong, then it is his fault, not yours.

## In-hand classes

On entering the ring, you will walk your horse, in line with all the others, round the edge of it in a clock-wise direction – that is, with your horse between the judge and yourself. (It is the horse he wants to look at.) Do not get too close to the horse in front. (He still wants to see your horse clearly.) Try to go at a reasonably smart pace, but naturally this depends on the others. Be prepared for a bit of stop-and-go, and cope with it efficiently. No one knows how many times you might have to go round. That depends partly on the size of the class, partly on the number of more or less equally good animals there are, and of course entirely on the judge.

Keep an eye on the ring steward, watching for his signal to take your place in the line. This is not particularly easy, for your horse's head will block your view of him. You do not want to be bobbing and weaving all the time, with consequent ill effects on the way your horse goes. Nor, on the other hand, do you want the steward to go frantic while you trundle round and round like a zombie.

When you are in line, remember that your position represents the judge's first impression only. He is now going to examine each exhibit at close quarters. Pay attention to your horse, and keep him alert. Do not let him rest a leg, like a loafer leaning against a lamp-post. Keep alert yourself. Do not pass the time chatting to the next chap.

Some judges, faced with a large class, line the horses up in two rows. The potential winners stand in front, and the obvious 'also-rans' in the second rank. This is a bad practice. It simplifies matters for him, no doubt, but it is demoralising to be relegated at once to the rubbish bin. If this happens to you, grin and bear it.

As the judge comes to your horse, say 'Good morning' to him (a smile does no harm) and answer any question he asks you. Otherwise, say nothing. His job is straightforward, though not easy – to decide, with the help of his eyes and hands, which is the best-made and soundest horse standing at that moment before him. He does not require ears, except to hear its breathing.

It is useless to tell him you won at the county show last week: he is probably contra-suggestible. He dislikes crude attempts to influence him. He is a judge because he also knows the subtler tricks, as well as he knows horses. He has been a competitor himself many times, and is not a fool. Many of the exhibitors will say afterwards that he *is* a fool, or biased, or even a rogue. But they will probably be wrong. The standard of sportsmanship has sadly degenerated, even in the heavy-horse ring, where it has always had a high reputation.

Let us assume you are in the gelding class. What is the judge looking for? A good commercial gelding. The one with the most presence. Sound in all his joints. The one that will command the highest price.

As he approaches, he will stop to estimate your horse's height. Then he will look at its mouth, its head, ears and eyes. In a junior class, he will consider whether it is the right age. (People have been known to get this wrong.) He will look over its body. He will feel each leg, back and front. (At least, he ought to. If he feels only one, that is wrong, but he might do it towards the end of a line if he is really tired.) He is looking for curbs, spavins, injuries, bumps and lumps and all the other things that might be amiss with those limbs which are so vital. He is also looking to see how good the feet are, and noting the shoeing.

All this while, you should stand perfectly still, and so should your horse. If he is a kicker, break your silence rule. The judge would appreciate being told 'He's a bit light behind' more than he would esteem an unheralded blow in the guts. He will not put your horse down for objecting to a stranger touching its feet; but he would put you down if the horse put him down. Finally he will have a good look from the rear.

Now he will pull out the first in the line and require him to come over near the ring-side and walk the horse away, parallel to the line of spectators (or the grandstand, if you are in exalted company), and walk back again and then to repeat the manoeuvre at a trot. This is to size up the horse's action from behind and in front, as he leaves and as he comes.

When it is your turn, walk your horse in a straight line for forty yards or so and turn him *away* from yourself – that is, right-handed. As you walk back, look directly *through* the judge so that your horse is walking at a uniform pace straight at him. He will get out of the way, because he expects you to do just that. Halt just before you are level with him. On the second little trip, your horse should break into a trot immediately and easily, and continue at a uniform pace. A good start is important. You have only a short distance to display a lively but collected action. Trot the horse back straight towards the judge, as when walking. Then halt again. Go back a few paces. Having moved aside twice, the judge does not want to be pushed round in a semi-circle while he ponders the excellence of your performance. Then return to your place in the line-up.

You might have a judge who tells you to make only one trip – walk away and trot back. But this is not a good idea. He really ought to be able to concentrate on the hind legs during the outward journey and on the front ones on the return, at each pace.

While waiting for the other competitors, stand well, and see that your horse does so. You are still on show before the public. You may have to walk round and round the edge of the ring again as before, while the judge finally makes his mind up.

At last, there you all are, in the order of merit that the judge thinks you deserve – unless he really cannot decide about the first two or three, in which case, if there is an official referee or a second judge who has been taking turns with him, he will obtain another opinion. He will not call for help if his only dilemma is whether to place you bottom or bottom-but-one. Your dress and demeanour might lift you from the end of the line.

If you have won a rosette, all you need to do is to take your hat off, shake hands, say 'Thank you very much' and put it up. These days, prizes are often presented by the wives of important men in companies which have generously sponsored the classes. She might put the rosettes up herself. Many of them nowadays have a clip at the back. If you find your horse starts swinging his head about, do not assume he has suddenly been afflicted with megrims or incipient rabies. The clip is probably sticking in his neck. Similarly, watch to see that the ribbons, which are sometimes very long, are not flapping in front of his face.

Some judges like to have a word with competitors, if they think it would be received in the right spirit. 'Your horse would have been third instead of fourth if it hadn't a big hock' is helpful. Even to the man at the bottom he might say kindly 'Not your day today, I am afraid, but thank you for coming.'

He might say nothing. Too many competitors may have been

glaring, or even muttering. It is not his duty to invite an insult. If he says anything to you, thank him pleasantly. If not, say nothing.

Take your correct place in the lap of honour. Do not exhibit the worst of ill manners by going straight out of the ring. Even if you are walking last, and especially if you have a grin on your face, there will be somebody in the crowd who likes you, and perhaps even your horse.

There might, there just *might*, be an opportunity afterwards to ask the judge for advice. He *might*, or might not, be inclined to cast you a pearl or two if he thinks you are a civilised beginner and genuinely want to improve. You will be surprised how well he remembers your horse, even if he has seen several classes since yours. But he is not obliged, even by courtesy, to discuss anything with you. And it is likely that he will depart pretty promptly after his work is done.

Incidentally, not every good judge is a good psychologist. Even at a third-rate show in a class of eight where five are hat-racks, he should examine the worst as gravely as the best, or should pretend to do so. There would be no show without the also-rans. And the owners of these are going to be discouraged if they are not taken seriously. It is a matter of courtesy – and psychology.

Half the fun of competing is, of course, to be in the ring with your own horse. But if your Trusty Adviser is a good showman, or your brother is sprightlier than you, consider the idea of letting them have a go. There is nothing in the rules about who does the showing. From the ring-side, you might learn how much you have failed to teach your horse.

Everything that has been said about showing a gelding applies also to a barren mare. But if your mare has a foal at foot, someone must take charge of the foal while you show the mare. The little one will have to come into the ring while its mother is being shown, otherwise it may kick up a terrible fuss. And the mother will put on a better show if she is not worrying where her offspring is. The foal can have a little practice in front of a crowd, but make certain that it goes well to one side, as well as behind, in order not to impede the judge's view. He will ignore the foal.

The same procedure applies when the roles are reversed, and it is the class for foals. The foal still goes behind the mare and to one side, but in returning to the judge it is the chap with the foal who makes a bee-line for him.

## Harness classes

The biggest shows in the heavy-horse calendar do not have harness classes. In those which do, horses are presented without a vehicle and are therefore in-hand. They wear shaft harness with a limited amount of additions by way of adornment. There are also decorated harness classes, where the horses are bedecked in a fantastic way with flowers and other finery, according to the fashion traditional to the district where the show takes place.

We have already spoken about these two degrees of embellishment. Here, we assume that if you are going to enter a harness class at all, it will not be in the decorated one, at least while you need this book to guide you. Do not add a little bit of something extra of your own devising to the basic decoration we have already listed. And it is better to have a few good brasses than a lot of rubbishy ones.

There have been small shows which, in the recent revival of heavy-horse interest, have attracted both ordinary and decorated entries to their one advertised 'harness class'. This poses a problem to the judge – most sensibly solved by dividing the class, at the last moment, into two, provided that the show society can produce the extra prizes and rosettes.

A harness class is for the 'cleanest and best appointed horses and gears'. 'Clean' means 'absolutely spotless', on the underside of all leather as well as on the outside. No dried tricklings of Brasso on the back of buckles! Impeccable in your own person, you will not know what 'clean' really means until you have examined the harness of the chap who has just won first prize. Clean becomes cleaner the further north you travel from the south coast. Scotsmen take studs out, clean them individually, and put them in again. They separate a bridle into what seems a thousand pieces, labour away at each one, and are even able to assemble the whole thing again.

All items of harness must also be serviceable and safe, must fit the horse that is actually wearing them, and must be perfectly adjusted. New harness, if not a cause for actual disqualification, will be a handicap. How can the judge decide how well you look after it, if it came from the saddler only yesterday?

'Clean' also means 'spotless' as far as the horse is concerned. No grease on his coat. The judge should be able to run his hand over any part of the animal and find it fit to pick up a cucumber sandwich with afterwards, if the secretary were to offer him one. The plaiting of mane and tail are naturally of the utmost importance, too.

There is no need to wear a bowler hat – an ordinary cap will do. You may look silly in it, but it is nice to have something to take off. Are you ready, now, to go in the ring? Much of what you will do is the same as in the in-hand classes. We shall mention only some special points.

In the preliminary walk round the ring, make doubly sure you give yourself plenty of room. Other horses swinging round might cause you to take emergency action and could mess up your harness.

When you are lined up in provisional order, and the judge reaches you, pay attention to what he is doing. There are two reasons. Firstly, you might learn something. Although he will maintain a poker face, you will see exactly what he is looking at and looking *for*: you will begin to realise why he is particularly long over one item, and quick over another. Secondly, he is more likely, in this class, to ask you a question. Your reply will be more sensible and brief if you have been watching intently enough to guess *why* he is asking. Confine your answer to what he wants to know.

He is not interested in whether you have been up all night cleaning the harness. If he asks how old some item is, he does not want its complete history. And he will not feel the legs. He is not judging the horse. He is judging you. When he reaches the end of the line, he may ask each man to walk his horse away and back, but not to trot him.

Some judges like to find an excuse to share the prizes round, especially at the smaller shows, where it is likely that one exhibitor belongs to a higher league than all the rest. And if he has brought more than one horse, he is the sort of man who will have two winners. The judge is conscious (and the show secretary even more so) that, if one or two chaps monopolise the awards, then everyone else is going to feel next year 'It's not worth going there. So-and-so will win everything. Or Such-and-Such.' He may therefore be delighted to gladden the heart of some deserving fellow who does not possess a glamorous show animal by putting him top in the harness class. Other judges would not dream of thinking like this. If the same man ends by winning everything, then so be it.

If there are only four or five competitors forward, even the sternest judge would like to be able to give a Commended rosette to the bottom man in the line. (He would hardly do that in a class of twelve, unless sheer quality forced him.) So: five competitors. You stand last. No disgrace in that. But the chap above you is commended, and you are not. That should make you think. Dirt? Ill-fitting harness? Collar wrong? You have failed badly somewhere.

## Turn-out classes

There are two sorts of turn-out classes – agricultural and commercial. The former is for any cart or waggon suitable to the occupation of farmer. You must not therefore have a sprung vehicle. Whether or not it has a high seat, for safety, may be your affair: but at some shows it is not allowed in this class. At some little shows, you may be permitted to take an implement along as a substitute for a vehicle. Examine the schedule.

By law, such vehicles going on a public road must have the owner's name and place of abode inscribed on them. Since they may all at some time go along a road, and since the show is simulating a real life situation, yours should be suitably painted with this legend. In any case, you are no doubt sufficiently proud of yourself to want to put it on. 'John Jones, Small Farm, Mudcombe' – that will look good. If you are not a farmer, just put 'John Jones, Mudcombe'.

A commercial turn-out should be a sprung vehicle with high seat, and proper to the trade declared on the side – or, if you are trying to get a bit of publicity, emblazoned on a board above your head. You should have a water bucket on the vehicle – preferably wooden, not galvanised or plastic. But you need not put any water in it. You should also have a nose-bag for each horse with some food in it. A waggon should have a drag-shoe and chain if it has no brake, and a roller scotch. And you yourself should have a whip and hold it while driving.

Your horse must be of a type suitable for the vehicle. This applies of course also to agricultural turn-outs, though there is less opportunity here of having some ridiculous combination of vehicle and horse-power.

Do not overload the harness with brasses. Some, but not too many. Remember that the harness, the shafts and so on all make it difficult to see the horse as a specimen animal. This gives you a chance to experiment with different sorts of bridle and pad. A change in either of these items can sometimes make a big difference in the over-all appearance of your horse.

In both types of class, you will also need a second human being to act as attendant. How should you both dress?

In an agricultural turn-out, you should try to look like farming types – prosperous farmers, if you can imagine the idea, on market day about to call on their bank manager. Not farmers called away from a mucky job. And not old-time farmers of the Thirties. We are in the Eighties.

Mr W. C. Saunders' team of Suffolks is unique among all breeds in two respects. No other private exhibitor shows an eight-horse turn-out: and it has a lady-driver, Miss Jenny Cauldwell (*Suffolk Horse Society*)

If you have a commercial turn-out, it is more difficult to be precise. Let's start with a bowler hat. You both ought to have one. Beneath that, it will depend on the nature of your business, and its size and reputation. If you are horsing a turn-out for a national company, then you should ask for a uniform before you sign the contract. But it would look bizarre if you and your colleague wore uniforms copied from Messrs Blank's Nationally Known Beers when your board said you were J. Robinson, Builder's Merchant, Casterbridge. In this latter case, wear a quiet suit.

The rest of our advice is applicable to both kinds of turn-out class. On going round the ring first time, do not get too close to the vehicle in front: you want to go, as far as possible, at your horse's normal walking pace, and certainly not to slow up every now and again. When you get in the line-up, your attendant should get down, stand at your horse's head and remain there.

The judge will check the harness to see whether it is suitable, sound, clean and fitting. He will also check the vehicle for its condition and safety. If it has woodworm, or if the shafts look likely to break any moment, it will not do. If it needs painting, or is badly painted, or

A modest agricultural turn-out

painted in absurd colours, this will count against you. You will be at
a disadvantage if its shape and construction are not authentic.

You will be asked to walk up and back, and also trot. In each case,
go at your horse's normal pace for each gait. Do not try to go too
fast. Fire engines used to be horse drawn, but if you have one of these,
you are unlikely to show it in a modern turn-out class, though you
might offer to put on a special display as a bit of fun. You may be
asked to back your vehicle. In fact, you should be, especially if the
judge can see that he is going to have difficulty in separating the
winners. Otherwise, the same advice applies as for other classes.
Make your horse stand properly when waiting, not resting a leg.

What relative importance does the judge place on all the many
elements – horse, harness, vehicle, man and so on? He has no scale of
marks to guide him, as you might think he has. He is just asked to
judge a turn-out, and he does it in his own way. So we cannot tell
you.

If he is in doubt whether to place A or B top, his decision will
presumably rest on which is the better horse. If they are both suitable
horses for the vehicles, it depends on how the horse *goes*. After all,
that is what it is all about. He may end up by favouring one because
the man has a tie and a hat on, and the other, without either, looks
slovenly. One man may look half asleep, or worried to death, whereas
the other is calm, collected and yet obviously alert. (Which one would
the judge prefer to go with all day, in dense traffic?)

Consider two top-class professional exhibitors at the same show.
In one case, the horses are experienced old campaigners. If you examined their legs, you might be surprised at the number of lumps and
bumps on them. But these do not incapacitate them, as you can see
from the way they go. The judge does not feel legs in a turn-out class.
The other competitor's animals are younger and inexperienced. Their
legs are unblemished. But their lack of experience means that they
make heavier weather of their work. The first lot win. But the younger
ones would stand above them in an in-hand class.

When moving round the ring at the end (or at the beginning) never
overtake the chap in front, even if he stops. But if he stops *and* asks
you to carry on, then do so. To go charging past another competitor
is unforgivable.

Finally, if you are nervous about showing in this class, do not show.
Find someone who can drive well and who is not nervous: you can be
the attendant in your own vehicle. Some people are so nervous as they
go in the ring that their hands are actually trembling. This is trans-

mitted right down the reins to the horse. He will go badly and, after a while, will not go at all. His own confidence is destroyed.

You are never going to feel sillier in your life than when your horses stop and refuse to budge, or when they start plunging about. The ring-side may love it, especially if the whole performance arouses an element of terror. And what would you do if the horse in front suddenly started bucketing about? Or if someone's pair bolted and seemed to be coming straight for you? Nowadays when so many people go in the ring before they have learned their job, it is a wonder that there have not been ghastly accidents.

When you do start exhibiting, begin with the local show, and climb the ladder as you gain confidence. If you happen to live near Kenilworth Castle, that does not mean that your local show is the Royal.

### Ploughing matches

A novice should begin with the smallest match, and enter the 'general purpose' class. 'High cut' needs a special plough, and is a specialist craft.

Even the experienced campaigner must study the rules in advance, if they are sent with the schedule, for they vary considerably from match to match. It is therefore useless to offer a specimen set here. Get your plough shining. A rusty one is a poor way to begin. And be equipped for emergencies. For example, if your plough-share breaks within minutes of starting, it is no good wishing you had brought a spare one.

Take food for your horse – and water, which may be a long way from where you are working, or even non-existent. For yourself, the organisers may supply a packed lunch, but if you are not sure of this, assume that they will not. And take someone with you, even if only to fetch and carry, hold your horses while you run to the beer tent, or hold them again half an hour later. He could also mark up your sticks for you, if he is the sort who can see if three sticks are in a straight line. Some people have zigzag vision.

Matches start earlier than most shows – at nine or nine-thirty. Arrive really early. If the rules have not been sent to you in advance, you will be told them. Plots will either be decided by drawing lots, or will have been allocated already. Yours might have some sort of obstacle, or a hole in it. It might conceal a crock of golden coins. Good or bad, you must take the luck of the draw.

You might face a totally different task from what you are accustomed to at home. You may find you are to plough stubble – or grassland. There is a vast difference between the two. You might be used to a sandy soil, or a beautiful loam – and find stony ground, or gravel, or chalk and flints. Or you might be lost simply because the land is so good, and you and your horses are unable to make the best use of it. You are not allowed to practise or have a trial run. But, chatting before the match starts, you will soon learn which competitors are local, and you may be surprised that one of them gives you some advice. If not, you can watch them, and learn a lot.

Even on the small plot that you have to deal with, the soil could vary two or three times. Set the plough as correctly as you can for a start, but remember you may have to change the share or coulter half-way down the first bout. It is the trouble you are prepared to take which will count. That is why you are given four hours. You could plough it much quicker, but this is an essay in perfection.

All the time the match is on, make certain that you do what your plot steward tells you. If you are given a minimum and maximum depth to plough at, try your best to keep within it. Make certain that any other rules are properly kept.

Your most difficult decision may be whether your helper should lead your horses. Some shows penalise you much more than others for this. You may take the view that, if you and your horses are inexperienced, it is better to lose fifty marks and have a go, rather than not to risk it at all. Novice horses, in any case, might jump all over your ploughing and lose you plenty of points that way. If they jump all over the next man's you will be highly unpopular, to put it mildly. If you have a really good man leading the horses, you can ignore the lines and concentrate entirely on the plough. This will be treated with contempt by the experts and, if there is tractor-ploughing also going on, it makes a bad advertisement for horse-ploughing!

This business of having assistance really began in the Fifties when people wanted to continue competing at matches, but had to borrow horses because they no longer had any of their own. Sometimes they would have a couple which had never seen each other before, and it was a matter of luck whether they would go all right together. One man borrowed two which could not understand a thing he said. They might have been totally deaf. He then discovered they were Welsh. In response to an appeal, a Welshman appeared from among the spectators, and talked them through beautifully.

We should not complain about anything that happens now if it is a result of those bad times. If it had not been for men obstinate enough

Colonel and Punch, two of Nick Rayner's horses, in a match with Eddy Dore at the plough (*Lee Weatherley*)

to persist with horse-ploughing matches in days when animals were going to the knackers in droves, there would be no horses at all today. Except at the top, standards may have dropped since the Thirties and before. They ought now to rise again, but it is slow progress. No one any longer spends day after day and all day walking behind a horse-plough to earn his living, which was the way to practise.

All in all, it will probably give you more satisfaction if you try to get round on your own. Ploughing-match people are different from show people. They are really helpful. It is not unlikely that the competitor next to you will help you through your first match. You will be for ever grateful. He could have made you feel so silly that you would never go near a match again. And yet, by his quiet help, he will have been instrumental in setting you off on a hobby that will give you years of good days out, enjoyable company and steady improvement until, one day, you win a prize. Of course, he will not help you to beat him. Even the real artist, the top-of-the-league ploughman, might help the tyro – but he would whip the share off as soon as he had finished and mix it up with all the others he has got, so that his closest rivals would not know what one he has used.

When you have competed a number of times, you will have met most of the common snags. For example, if you and your neighbour happen to be close together, your horses are quite likely to interpret a command that he gives as one that comes from you. They will start, or stop, when he tells his pair to do so.

If anything goes really wrong, or you have a breakdown, tell your steward. A good excuse might save you losing points for finishing late. If you want to give up completely, you will be allowed to do so, provided you ask him nicely if he minds. It is not a crime, like walking out of the show ring. You will probably forfeit your transport money, but that is only reasonable.

The actual ploughing is not necessarily the only competition of the day. There might be a turn-out class, or class for best mare or gelding, judged either before or during the match. Some societies award prizes for the best working teams. These are far more glorious to win than any of the others (except those for ploughing), because they are for horsemanship. Some of the experts turn up with working harness because they are interested only in the match. Other men, who would never win for ploughing, aim for one of the other awards and turn out accordingly, though of course they have to plough.

A match is decided on points, allotted for every part of the work. This makes for good competition, because, if you have made a mistake at the very start, you cannot obliterate it. Your first ten yards, when it is done, is done, for all to see. Sometimes the points are published on a board. You can see where you have done badly, or well, and then go back to look at your work. It is instructive to look at the winners' scores, too, and then examine their work.

However, before you creep off to conduct your post-mortem or wait for the prize-giving, consider your horses. They are probably hot, and possibly tired (certainly so if they are not in regular work). It may be raining. It might be windy. You will probably be away an hour. Do not leave them tied up. Put them up in the lorry, put rugs on them if necessary, and let them have a hay-net.

With a clear conscience, you can now go and drink your beer and talk to other people. You will learn more in one day here than in a couple of years at home. Ask, and you will be answered. You will be given positive advice, as well as plenty of suggestions about where you have gone wrong. Weigh it all up. A few words from the man who has won will be better than a hundred from someone who is as green as you are but hides his complexion behind the size of his mouth.

The judges, too, are perhaps more likely to have time and inclination to tell you about your errors than those at a show. One of the things that makes a ploughing match a marvellous education is that mistakes and skills are open to analysis afterwards. It is as good as a slow motion play-back of an incident in football or cricket.

Finally, as you leave the ground, you will not lack assistance to load up your plough. In your turn, you can no doubt offer a helping hand to some of the good folk among whom you have spent an instructive day.

At home, work on your weak points. You may be reminded what these are, if the society sends you through the post, as some do, a detailed record of the scoring.

You might even discover that you have your horses the wrong way round. Try changing over the land horse and the furrow horse. Some take to walking the furrow as if they were born to it. Others will do it half-heartedly, and be inclined to put a foot up on the ploughing. Put them where each goes better, not where they look better. Ploughing is a craft, and it is by the finished product that it must be judged.

A Percheron and a Shire drilling corn at a spring 'working' *(Anne Ford-Lloyd FRPS)*

## Workings

These are a modern invention. The first, organised by the Southern Counties Heavy Horse Association (then called the S C Horse Plough-ing Association), was held in 1972 at Broadley Farm, Wootton, in the New Forest. They are fun-events. In pre-tractor days, it would not have been regarded as fun to take one's horses to some other farm and start working there on the Sabbath.

Workings serve three purposes. They provide a good day out for the horse-owners – congenial fellowship and an opportunity to talk shop. They publicise the heavy horse, attracting the general public in enormous numbers. And they bring in a lot of cash, either for charity or for insurance against a rainy day next year, or both.

There is no set pattern of events and activities. Every society does its own thing. Some workings are well organised: others, less so. Some societies efficiently inform and amuse the public, while others have much to learn about keeping the customers happy and their minds occupied.

An element of competition is introduced at some events. There might be, for example, a sort of pentathlon consisting of a bit of ploughing, harrowing, mock-drilling, backing a cart, and driving round a mild 'obstacle course' with posts representing gateways. But you need not go in for the competitive part.

For the beginner, a working is the best way of learning all sorts of things as well as of making friends with other horse-owners, who will give you advice that they would never impart if you met them at a show. The atmosphere is relaxed and the dread of making a fool of yourself is almost removed.

Ring the secretary and find out whether he wants you to bring show or working harness. If the latter, do please clean it up. If the former, ask if you should do the mane and tail up: even if not, please do bring your horse well groomed and clean. You will be on view, even if not on show. There will be no judge, but the public is capable of judging whether you take pride in yourself and your horses. Tell the secretary if you can bring any implements or vehicles of your own, and enquire what he needs to achieve a balance. He will appreciate this sort of co-operation. He probably receives little of it. But do not put yourself down for any task that you have never done before.

A special feature of workings is that visitors are allowed to have a go themselves with horses, and the bolder spirits love this. But you are under no obligation to be one of those who permit it. You can always pretend that this is your horse's first time out and you are unsure of his reaction, or that, although he looks dopey, he is actually so difficult that you are the only man in England who can manage him.

Spend a reasonable proportion of the day actually doing something. Do not stand about all the time talking to your friends. The public will not even know what the implement lying on the ground is for, unless you use it. And when they ask what you are doing, tell them. Some participants do a great job at these workings – going up and down, harrowing the same old piece of ground again and again, and talking and joking with the customers. They make up for the other sort.

If it starts raining, carry on and do your best – as long as there are even a few people prepared to stay on the ground. You are being paid your transport money, and you are probably a member of the society running the event. If not, you ought to be. Or perhaps you belong to a similar society fifty miles away, which would like these chaps here to come and support your event next month.

Almost more than at any other event, it is good to have someone with you to share the work and the responsibility, and therefore the enjoyment. You can each have a breather, watch the other chaps, and

Nick Rayner's Broadley Colonel, one of the team used by the late Jack Pearce, champion horse ploughman, taking his body on its final journey *(Lee Weatherley)*

talk to them. A working is a sort of organised chaos, and its free-and-easy atmosphere, with participants and public intermingling, implies that all is safe for everyone. At a formal show, there is no such suggestion. You therefore have a special duty not to leave your horse unattended, even if there is only a slight possibility of his misbehaving or taking off at the click of a camera.

Before you go home, thank the secretary and others who have worked hard. But do not forget the good fellow who has allowed all these people to come and have a day out on his farm.

## Carnivals, fêtes and funerals

If you are invited to bring your horse and vehicle to a carnival or fête, and especially if the carnival queen is to ride with you, you might be tempted to accept without due thought. Find out more about it. Are they going to fill your waggon with a lot of other girls as well? If they are, you might agree at once. But you must assess the safety of the whole operation.

Discover exactly where the procession starts from, where it ends and (most important of all) the route. The organisers will not know what is involved in driving a waggon through crowds. So do not allow yourself to be trapped in the dilemma of either having to go down a steep and slippery tarmac hill with a full load of beauty or going on strike at the last moment, incurring the wrath of the whole township. And if they want you to go *up* a hill, that could be worse. Carnivals are stop-go affairs. Will they halt half-way up the one-in-six High Street? Should you be in any doubt about anything, walk the whole route yourself. Get every detail tied up. Then, if you accept, prepare to enjoy yourself.

The same initial caution should apply to funerals. Old So-and-So has died and the family wants him to be drawn by horses to his grave, because in his young days he was a fine horseman and his mind often went back to those old times. His waggon is still on the place, but there are no horses, and no one to drive them even if there were. Will you oblige?

The vehicle must, of course, *be* a waggon, preferably without high sides. A cart is no good. You will be leading the horse, not driving him. Pick a slow walker. Traditionally, he should be black, or the nearest you can get to it, and you should use black decorations for mane and tail. But people nowadays do not wear funereal clothes and logically there is no reason why the horse should conform to the custom of years ago. So whatever you do, you are bound to be out of line somewhere – either with horse-custom or modern (rather, let us say enlightened and Christian) notions of a funeral.

Discuss the matter carefully with the family, and work out the whole procedure with the undertaker. If you think you will make a mess of the job, say so. And do check that old waggon they talked about. One kind chap, entering thoughtlessly into a funeral engagement, got only half-way to the church before the wheels collapsed and the deceased was unceremoniously tipped out on to the roadway.

# 9

# Breeding and Young Life

'Some people buy champion horses. I prefer to breed them myself.' So spoke once, and not intending to be quoted, one of the greatest experts of his time on cart-horses, King George V himself. If showing represents the culmination of ambition for some, breeding no doubt scales the final height in the hopes of others.

### Choosing a stallion

One thing is certain. If you want a foal, you cannot ask your vet for a packet of seed. A stallion is going to have physically to cover your mare, because insemination is not practised in the world you are entering. Perhaps you think it ought to be. There you are, at Mud-combe-in-the-Suburbs, without the faintest idea where any stallions are, or which would be the best one even if you did. Why can you not ring the vet, and ask him to give your mare a shot of no. 21 or 43 in a catalogue?

The successful raising of cattle is a matter of improving the milk or beef yield of whole herds. The individual cow's merit is less important than the general performance of the group; and the group is a tiny part of a national product counted in hundreds of thousands. In contrast, the breeding of Thoroughbred race-horses is a ceaseless quest for the perfect individual that can run faster than all others. The humble cart-horse is in the same category as the bluest-blooded member of his species – for several reasons, not the least of them being that insemination would stimulate such a demand for the semen of a very few closely related sires of outstanding merit that the whole genetic future of the breed concerned would be thrown very soon into jeopardy. You must therefore find a stallion. What sorts are there to choose from?

Every stallion must possess a licence from the Ministry of Agriculture, Fisheries and Food. This ensures that, in the opinion of the official Veterinary Inspector, he is of good conformation and free of a number of hereditary unsoundnesses. It does not necessarily mean that he is in the pedigree register of any particular breed society. If he is (and most are), that does not of itself give him any extra claim to individual excellence. But it does enable you to look up his ancestry in the male and female lines, probably over many generations, and research the qualities of the animals figuring in his genealogy.

By studying this tree, you may detect the extent to which he is 'closely' bred. Several doses of one particularly good line of blood may give you confidence about his prepotency – that is, his ability to pass on his characteristics (bad as well as good), even via the medium of nondescript and unsystematically bred mares. Unless he is very young, you will also have the opportunity of discovering what sort of progeny he has obtained from the pure-bred mares of his breed. By enquiry, you might also obtain some idea as to his actual fertility.

Too many good young horses have been castrated because it is the easy way out for their owners. Such a good price has been offered for them to make show geldings that it is tempting to take the money that is certain rather than the uncertainty that attends stallion-ownership. Therefore, to encourage the retention of good horses as sires, the breed societies offer premiums. A pedigree stallion that has a premium is therefore a very good proposition. If he is also a winner of prizes, better still. If many of his offspring are prizewinners too, he is a horse of the topmost class.

Between the most and the least fashionable of stallions there is, obviously, a difference of fee. But, compared with the cost of buying and keeping a mare, this should not influence you; the dearest might cost twice as much as the cheapest, but not a hundred times more.

Do not make the mistake, however, of thinking that only the current Adonis of your breed can possibly be good enough for you. Let us assume your mare is a Shire (simply because there are more of these than any other, ranging from the really 'common' one that is but vaguely Shire-type to the blue-blooded beauty whose name and ancestry have been recorded in the breed's Debrett). If she is deficient in size, substance and pedigree papers, just the horse for her might be Joe Bloggs' – a bit old-fashioned and chunky, and no oil-painting, but strong in those points where she is weak. The foal might be what folk would call a 'proper horse': should it be a filly, she might have foundations which, allied to a top-class stallion, could produce a grand-daughter of great merit. If in the first place you had used the leading stallion of the day, the result might have been disappointing: some 'quality' but too little substance.

Do avoid a stallion that is funny-tempered. And do use one that is registered in his stud-book. This might give you the chance to discover the temperament of his sire and dam, as well. And, if you get a filly-foal, she can put her hoof on the pedigree ladder.

You would do well to study colour also, at least in the Shire and Clydesdale breeds. If you are looking for a Suffolk or Percheron stallion, of course there is no colour problem.

Heredity of coat colour remains, in practice, almost as chancy a business now as it did a hundred years ago. The only certainties are that a chestnut mated to a chestnut is bound to produce a chestnut, and that you cannot produce a grey unless one of the parents is a grey and you probably will produce a grey if both are grey. This accounts for the certainty that the Clydesdale breed, having got itself very largely roan, will go on becoming 'roaner and roaner' unless a lot of other blood is introduced.

Theoretically, one ought to be able to go further than that, because much is known now about genetics. For example, we know that the reason why two chestnuts must produce a chestnut is that this colour is recessive – like blue in the human eye. But bay (including the very dark version we usually call brown) and black might be either true or hybrid.

Even under experimental conditions, it would be very difficult to know whether (say) a bay Shire were pure or hybrid. If the same bay horse were mated to the same bay mare every year, and a foal was produced every year, as soon as a chestnut one appeared it would be certain that either the stallion or the mare was a hybrid bay. But which? If the experiment lasted ten years, and ten bay foals resulted, there is no guarantee that the eleventh foal will not turn out chestnut. No mare can have enough foals to remove the doubt, which is almost as great as it was a century ago because new blood, less than truly pure, has constantly been coming in through 'grading-up'.

But where are the stallions? Where is any stallion? Some will remain next season on the premises of their owners. Others will be let out to hiring societies or to individuals, perhaps at the opposite end of the country. (The societies, well-organised co-operatives of mare-owners in certain districts, are now confined to the Shire breed.)

Approach the secretary of the appropiate breed society. He will be able to tell you who owns what stallions, and where those stallions will be next season. Incidentally, do become a member of the breed society yourself. On the grounds of economy alone, this is virtually essential if you are likely to aim at pedigree or grade status for your animals. In addition, you will receive far more help and make many more contacts with other owners than the annual subscription would suggest. You do not have to own a blue-blooded horse, or for that matter any horse at all, in order to join.

If there is a hiring society in your area, join it. If there is any other society concerned with the use and promotion of heavy horses any-where near you, join that, too – or even a society whose interests are only partially to do with heavy horses. From newsletters and personal contacts with members at shows and meetings, you will soon find out where the more localised and obscure stallions are, and what they are like.

There may be a stallion almost round the corner from you. Because people do not put entire horses out in a field near the main road, you will not have seen him. And because they are not advertised in the weekly paper, like light horse and pony sires, you will not have heard of him. Nor will the secretary of the local show know much about this, but he will be able to tell you who the leading exhibitors are and, by ringing them, you can learn a lot.

You will not be doing all this in a hurry. Breeding will be in your mind a couple of years before you actually go in for it. So, in fact, you will not need to ring up the local show secretary after all. By going to shows and treasuring the catalogues in which you have made notes ('Good gelding – Bumble bred it himself – nice chap'), you will know who to go to for advice if, as the breeding season approaches, you still have not tracked down the stallions, far or near, to which you might put your mare.

### Watching your mare

During the winter the mare's sexual organs are, literally, closed to business. In spring, perhaps late in March, things begin to happen. Around just one of the many egg-cells present in each of her two ovaries, a fluid-filled sac develops and grows. It swells so much that eventually it bursts, and the egg is sent into the passage that leads to the womb (uterus). If in this fallopian tube a live sperm-cell from the stallion reaches and penetrates it, that is conception. The fertilised egg now travels to the end of the tube and into the womb, where it attaches itself to the uterine wall.

If, however, for any reason conception does not take place, the egg will die within a few hours. The same ovary or the other one will try again later, and another ripened follicle surrounding one of the egg-cells will burst twenty-one days later (give or take a day or so) and a new egg will be sent into the appropriate fallopian tube. In the absence of conception, this cycle will continue until early autumn, after which shop is shut until the following spring.

Sometimes, two eggs are released in the same period, but not necessarily at the identical moment: there might even be an interval of a couple of days. This used to be considered a rare event, but it is now realised that at some times in some mares double ovulations are not infrequent. The mare therefore has the unusual ability to conceive two entirely separate embryos – not identical twins, and perhaps not twins at all in the accepted sense of the term, because they can originate from two matings with different stallions, possibly two days apart in time. The two embryos will develop in the womb independently, each in a different 'bag'.

In practice, double conceptions occur far less often than double ovulations. And they are not a good thing. In the vast majority of cases, one of the two embryos is aborted and, if this happens early on, the owner of the mare may not have the slightest idea what has happened. Even if both foals go the full term and both are actually born alive, one – or both – will be unlikely to survive. The mare is not geared to the successful production of more than one offspring at a time.

The stallion's semen contains many millions of sperm – thousands of millions in a good horse. Some are dead and some imperfect – fertility varies from one animal to another and from time to time, and is not synonymous with virility. But, unless there is something really wrong with him, that still leaves millions of lively wrigglers, most of them robust enough to live in the mare for several hours or even up to a couple of days, provided that adverse conditions or infection inside her do not cause a quick massacre. Surely one of this vast army will choose the correct tube, propel itself up there and find that egg?

However, if we view the job from the outside, as indeed we must, it is not so simple. The outward and visible sign of a follicle developing is the behaviour of the mare. She may become excitable and, if you touch her anywhere at the rear end, she will probably squeal and make to kick. As time goes on, she will tend to stand with her legs straddled and her tail lifted. After staling, mares always open and close the lips of the vulva for a few moments, but if she starts 'winking' like this in conjunction with her other attitudes, it is an infallible sign that she is in season.

Some mares do not 'show' as much as others; a few hardly show at all. Any doubts you may have can probably be resolved if you have a gelding to sniff around her. This will probably induce her to start, though a wink is no better than a nod to a cut horse.

If mares were controlled by an electric instead of a glandular time-clock, this period of heat would last five days. Let us assume, for the moment, that it does. In the early stages, in spite of her behaviour, she is unlikely to turn her quarters to the stallion. She will kick at him if he starts to pay attention to her. This is not merely playing hard-to-get, but is biologically sensible, because the egg will not be released until the end of the third day. After ovulation, she begins to 'go off' and in forty-eight hours the heat has ceased entirely.

Unfortunately, the duration of oestrus (heat) is variable and unpredictable. It may last four days, or eight. The first heat of the season may be very prolonged indeed, and so lukewarm as to be scarcely detectable, especially in maiden mares. As high summer approaches, it will be shorter and more intense. The basic problem is that one is attempting to have the mare served not three days after the beginning of heat, but two full days before the end of it – an entirely different matter, and often difficult to determine.

In the wild, a stallion will serve a mare several times during the period that she will allow him to do so – perhaps many times, depending on his virility and the number of other mares claiming attention. One of these occasions will possibly be successful. If not, there is always the next oestrus. But the domesticated mare for many reasons is not allowed to conceive in this care-free way, and her owner will also have a reason for desiring her to do so at a time of year convenient to him.

The Thoroughbred mare, from whom it is hoped to produce a winner of races, begins her breeding season as soon as possible after 15 February, which entails all sorts of efforts to bring her into season earlier than would normally happen. Since she carries her foal eleven months, the little money-spinning marvel might be born as early as the middle of January. Every horse officially becomes a yearling on the following 1 January after it is born, and an animal that is actually twenty-eight months old clearly has a better chance of doing well in a June race for two-year-olds than one that is four or five months younger. (A foal prematurely born on 31 December is a disaster, because the next day it becomes, on paper, one year old.)

Breeders of cart-horses face a more complex set of considerations. For reasons rooted in economy and commonsense, both mare and foal are going to live as naturally as possible. The owner does not want a birth when all is covered in deep snow and no grass grows. But he does want both mother and child to have the longest possible period together of good weather and good herbage, which are excellent for the mare's milk, so that he can wean a strong well-grown foal in the autumn. In addition, if he shows the mare and hopes that the foal will be good enough to show also, he does not want her out of action in the middle of June or her foal to be too small and undeveloped in competition with older babies at the later shows.

The ideal time for birth is one consideration. The most promising month for conception is another. This is certainly May. In that month, oestrus will without doubt culminate in ovulation, even if in earlier heats none of the egg follicles has actually ripened. After May, the likelihood of ovulation begins gradually to diminish. No doubt mother nature, in thus operating accelerator and brake, is acting for the best according to her lights.

Since the first heat might last ten, twelve or possibly even twenty days in a languid and barely discernible way, it is possible that you will deliberately give this one a miss. But mark well the day on which she 'goes off'. Add twenty-one days to that, and you should have the date on which she finishes the second time. Now assume that the next heat will be a five-day one, and add only sixteen days instead. If she does begin to show on that sixteenth day or the day after, you have some pretty accurate idea of what is going on inside her. It could be that a service on the nineteenth day would be 'spot on'.

If your mare were allowed only one service for the money, your possible expenses would be something to worry about. But for your one fee the wretched stallion-owner agrees that his horse should cover your mare again if necessary – and, if still necessary, again and again and again.

He wants your mare in foal as much as you do, because if she remains barren you might go round moaning that his stallion is no good. Also, he would like her in foal as quickly as possible, in order to get at least one customer off his hands. There is nothing more troublesome, as June comes in, than a whole crowd of mares still not 'stopped'.

But, which is it to be? A local horse, or will you have to send her away? The decision may lie between Joe Bloggs' ol' 'oss just down the road and John Proe's beautiful stallion a hundred miles off. If this is so, it is probably the distant one that you really want, and the only attraction of the local horse is convenience and economy. (In actual fact, your dilemma will not be so simple. For example, the nearest stallion may be twenty miles distant, not down the road. But it will be easier to explain matters if we assume this to be the position.)

Whichever you choose, make sure your mare is in good physical condition. Not too fat: fat ones are hard to get in foal. Nor too thin: plain mares are difficult, but not so difficult as fat ones. Take her hind shoes off and, if they need it, have the hind hooves trimmed. The stallion-owner aims not to have his horse kicked at all, but certainly not with an iron shoe or pointed hoof.

Let us first see what happens if you have selected Joe Bloggs' horse. After that, we can consider what is involved should you decide to send the mare away to Proe's. The complications that arise, whether she goes to Bloggs' or Proe's, if she already has a foal at foot, are discussed on page 193.

## The local horse

Your mare has had an early heat which you have done nothing about, but you have worked out when she should come on again. You have already made an arrangement with Mr Bloggs. (In exalted circles, this is called 'securing a nomination'.) Now ring him and tell him that this should be, say, next Wednesday. It might be agreed that you will bring her along after tea on Friday. But things are delayed and, after another talk, it is arranged for before breakfast on Monday.

You can walk there if it is only two or three miles. If twenty, you will have to arrange transport. Fifty is expensive. Have a good halter on your mare, with a long rope, so that you can really hold her. Awaiting you will be Mr Bloggs. He will hold his horse. You will hold your mare.

On arrival, ask him what he wants you to do. Carry out his requests to the letter. He might tell you to take the mare round the corner a moment. He knows his horse, and he knows his own methods. He will first 'try' your mare. You will have to stand holding her on one side of a suitable barrier. He brings the horse up on the other side. You both watch while the two animals touch muzzles, snort, sniff, and so on. Then you will bring her parallel to the barrier and close to it. Do not stand in front of her: she might strike with a fore-foot if she resents the stallion. Stand beside her, level with her shoulder. The horse will now work his way down to her quarters, with many a strange excited exclamation and nibble.

Even you may realise, from your mare's reaction to all this, that she wants to be covered. But leave it to Bloggs. He has seen many a mare at a trying board and has developed a sixth sense about whether she might change her mind – one way or the other. If he thinks that the affair can be safely consummated, he will tell you where to take her. Your job, again, will be to hold her and, if she is a maiden mare, to reassure her, so that nervousness does not impede her desire. It is Bloggs, and his horse, who are taking the risks because if, after all, she decides to kick out, then she will. A stallion is a fearsome creature, but at a mating it is the mare who can be lethal.

If old Bloggs does have some assistant, his function might be to see that the mare's tail is kept to one side and to make sure the horse finds the right place. It might seem absurd that there should be any doubt about this until you remember that his penis is different from that of other farm animals. It requires enlargement through the action of muscle and the infusion of blood: it is also free of the body, not encased for much of its length by the outer skin of the belly. Consequently, it is very large and not completely manageable until rigid.

You must make certain that your mare does not move forward as the horse comes down, because it would not be amusing if he bumped his chin on her quarters. A false start may set up all sorts of unmanageable reactions from both horse and mare and you do not want to be responsible for a mêlée, but after an adroit connexion the job will proceed smoothly. When you see the horse completely motionless, he is ejaculating. After he dismounts, you will be told to walk her away, and to keep her walking, in order to prevent her from 'straining' much of the semen out.

Joe may decide that it would be a good idea to serve her again. If so, he will return the stallion to the box and request you to take the mare somewhere out of sight. You may be invited in for a cheering cup and after, say, three quarters of an hour, the horse will be brought to her again. Who are you to decline either of these kind offers? But in point of fact, a double dose on the wrong day will achieve nothing much compared with a single one at the right time.

A further covering, the next day or the day after that, would probably be the best – though, for all you and Joe know, that might be too late and you have chosen exactly the fruitful moment. If you have driven fifty miles, you may not have time to make another journey, and Joe will not want to bring the horse to your place. He might fear that you do not have the right set-up. His stallion is a valuable animal. And he might not have time to cart the horse round the countryside, because he is first and foremost a farmer.

Your mare now 'goes off'. Work out when her next heat should begin, and watch her carefully, not just that day but for several days afterwards. If time passes and she does not come on, all should be well. Ring Joe and tell him the glad tidings. But should she start again, arrange to repeat the performance.

If after that she comes into oestrus once more, bad luck. Have her served again. But you might consider also telling your vet. There could be some infection or physical peculiarity preventing pregnancy. Perhaps you think a different stallion might do the trick. That would mean a new fee, of course. And it probably would not be of any use.

What is almost certainly wrong is not Joe's horse or your mare at all, but this matter of timing. In the days before the veterinary profession was able to ascertain the nature of the problem, there was every justification for the pious hope that provided the mare was eager to accept the stallion, a good job had been done. Together with the stallion-owners' rule (an absurd one, but nobody was to know it) that mares should not be covered twice in the same heat, that accounted for the very low conception rate of years ago. Nowadays, although to achieve correct timing is often extremely difficult in so erratic a creature as a mare, there is no excuse for ignoring biological facts. It may be that old Joe, good practical man though he may be, is one of those (and there are still many) who do not trouble their heads over this matter and who are responsible for the average rate of conception still being lower than it should be. If so, you are in a dilemma (for he will not take kindly to suggestions from a beginner) if you want the second covering two days later and he does not.

But supposing she is apparently stopped? Do not assume she is safely in foal. Keep watching her, and turn to page 188.

### Away to stud

John Proe's horse is standing at home this season, a hundred miles from you. He is the sire of your dreams. Perhaps 'dreams' is the right word, because you may never have set eyes on the creature. That does not really matter, as long as you have made all proper enquiries, and men whose judgment is better than yours are in favour of your spending the money – possible twice the fee charged by Joe, plus travelling and board residence.

Proper enquiries? How much do you know about the Proe establishment? Sad to say, unless the world has changed for the better, there may still be stallion-owners who will not treat your mare with the loving care she receives from you.

Such men would let her pick a meagre living on some dusty old worn-out pasture, and send her home after several weeks looking like a hat-rack. The man who would do this (*can* there be any, now?) might also fail to be meticulous in seeing that she is given the best chance of conception. His horse could perhaps stop her straight away if the mating were timed correctly, but slack organisation means that he will probably not, and she will hang around for weeks while you pay good money for bad keep. The dream becomes a nightmare if you suspect that, in the haphazard (or knavish) course of things there, the horse that does get your mare in foal at the last is not the stallion of your choice at all, but some other which you would have refused if old Joe had offered him to you. Such men do not enhance their reputation, and are long-term fools, but they may still exist.

Luckily Mr Proe is a first-class man. He will look after your mare better than you can, provided he is happy about accepting her. Perhaps you had not thought of that side of it?

He has an outstanding horse. Its reputation depends upon the foals it fathers. What sort of foal will he get out of a half-bred half-sized mare of strange hue and homely shape? If yours is one of these, Mr Proe will not be keen. However, stallions are expensive to keep, even with the help of a premium, and do not do half the business these days that they could. So Proe will probably want your fee. Being the sort of man he is, he will treat your mare as well as the current breed champion. After all, your money is as good as anyone else's. (It is no use asking for a discount on the grounds that your Dolly is only half the mare that X's is.)

Mr Proe will want to know as much about Dolly as you can tell him – her breeding history if she has one and, if not, whether she is barren from last year or a maiden. You must tell him about her recent health; and about any peculiarities of temperament or behaviour, either in general or when introduced to a stallion.

When you have worked out when she will probably be coming on, ring him up. It may be best to send her (minus shoes and plus a good head collar) a week before the heat is due to begin, to give her a chance to settle down. A sudden transfer to strange surroundings can bring an upset to the normal pattern of oestrus. On the other hand, if you can persuade someone else near you to send his mare there, it would save money to tie in with him. The same applies if any other opportunity of cheap transport arises.

Proe will probably worm her on arrival, even if you tell him you have treated her regularly. He will also check that she is not suffering from a contagious disease, including the dreaded equine metritis, that she might pass on via the stallion to all the other mares subsequently served. The fussier he seems to be, the more you should be pleased. (This is not to suggest that old Joe will not bother about any of these precautions. But some of them – for example, worming – will not apply to quick visits.)

If there is anything wrong with your mare, he will be prompt to tell you. After all, you might be the sort of person whose first reaction is to blame him for what is not his fault. He has to play safe. To one highly-respected stallion-owner it became apparent, after a day or two, that a mare received from a first-time customer was thinner than when she arrived. Within a week, she was obviously wasting. His telephone calls to her owner were received first with disbelief, next with untactfully worded suggestions that she was not being properly fed, and finally with abuse. As it turned out, the mare was suffering from a contagious disease and the stallion-owner's vet had to ring the oafish owner of the mare and almost melt the telephone wires before he got the message across. Such experiences are rare, but just one is sufficient to make a Proe cautious.

There is little more to be said. The very fact that you have sent Dolly to John Proe relieves you of all bother. You pay the fee, and the transport. You pay for her keep, which will vary according to how much grass there is at the time, the current cost of hay, and so on. And you pay veterinary and other necessary expenses. Good old Proe, and his horse, do the rest.

When does she come home? You should allow six weeks, but it is a matter of weighing probabilities. You want only one transport bill, and you want a foal. If she keeps returning to the horse, you might be advised to leave her longer, pay for veterinary examination and perhaps also for an injection to bring another heat along early. Take John's advice.

When she does return home, looking fit and well, write and thank him. If, next spring, after all the good omens and expense, there is no foal, do not blame him. Buy him a drink if you track him down at a show. He might give you a reduced fee this second year, after a barren result before. But if you cannot stand the disappointment, take up breeding rabbits or white mice. They are easier than mares, though less interesting and not so good in harness.

## Is she pregnant?

Sometimes, a mare that has conceived will resorb the embryo. So, after missing one or two heats, she might then come on again later in the season – perhaps too late. At other times, there is a failure to come into 'use' simply because the yellow body (if you are fond of Latin, call it the *corpus luteum*) outstays its welcome. This covers the hole on the ovary left by the burst egg follicle and produces a hormone that is responsible for maintaining pregnancy. Unless the mare is actually in foal, it should stop working after about seventeen days. But if it obstinately persists, there can be no heat. You think your mare is pregnant, and she is not.

Your vet can check pregnancy in three ways, depending on when he does it – manually through the rectum at about six weeks, by blood testing from 45 to 100 days after the last service, or, after about four and a half months, by urine samples. Which method he chooses is for him to decide.

If he says the mare is pregnant, then she almost certainly is. If she does not in due course produce a foal, do not blame him. She must have aborted it. When, you may never know. You might just not notice a tiny foetus somewhere in a field. Foxes have been known to seize upon larger ones. Upon such grisly happenings we shall not dwell, nor shall we suggest why a foal may be 'slipped'. This is a matter for your vet. In any case, if you let him take charge of your mare's welfare in the first place, he will be in a better position to remove some possible causes of abortion, as also of failure to conceive.

If, however, he 'arms' the mare after six weeks and finds her not in foal, and then discovers that no follicle is ripening and no heat imminent, he can give an injection to get things moving. Sometimes, just to be awkward, a follicle does ripen in the proper way, but the mare fools her owner by having a 'silent heat', which from her behaviour is undetectable.

Your own eyes will not confirm pregnancy until the New Year, if then. In-foal mares may become a little heavier, more ponderous. The belly of an older one, that has had foals before, may tend to drop and perhaps to become a little wider on one side than the other. The young mare, carrying her first produce, will be more likely to retain her youthful shape. On the other hand, even experienced horsemen may mistake 'grass fat' acquired in spring for pregnancy. If you can feel something kicking inside, what else can it be but a foal? If you cannot, it does not mean that there is nothing there. It is not surprising that mares are sold 'believed in foal'. 'In foal' constitutes a warranty.

Just as experienced men have believed a foal to be on the way when there was not, so others have bought apparently barren mares and discovered the error only when, one morning, they were astounded to find a little stranger in their midst. A certain elderly mare seemed to have come to the end of a prolific breeding career, so her owner, unable to keep her and not wishing to send her to the knacker, sold her to a good man for the princely sum of £1, plus VAT. Late the following spring and without warning, the old dear dropped a foal. They say that it is ungracious to look a gift horse in the mouth, but if a vet had looked this one in the womb, he would have seen a jewel indeed, for when the colt was two he was sold to a customer in the United States for £5000.

## Birth

Your mare is, you believe, pregnant. Do not wrap her in cotton-wool. She can lead her normal life. A little steady work will do her no harm. Starting a two-ton load on a hill, or any other severe strain, would be a silly thing to ask her to do, but she probably never has to do that anyway. As winter comes on, watch the feeding to see that her condition is kept up. Do not let her become too fat. But it is worse if she is thin. Make sure she can have plenty of exercise. Do not keep her standing indoors all the time.

From the New Year, she will want something better than plain fare. And cut out shaft work. The danger lies not in pulling, but in backing. You do not want to encourage an abortion. But she can go in chains almost until foaling-time, provided you are sensible.

The gestation period in mares is normally 340 days. Reckon them up from the last service and mark the date on your calendar. But mares are not machines; they are unpredictable in all their ways. Yours might have her foal two or three weeks before you expect it, or a similar time later. A foal born more than four weeks early is regarded as premature, and may not live. So start watching her pretty carefully before even ten months.

If her udder grows bigger, at first after she has been resting, and then constantly, her time is growing near. If a sticky wax, formed from slightly oozing milk, appears on her teats, she is nearer still. If this disappears and she begins actually to drip milk at times, she is almost due. But she may not noticeably 'bag up' at all. You just do not know. Visit her more and more frequently, especially at night. It is very unlikely that she will foal in the daytime. Mares are secretive about this business and have an amazing ability to delay delivery until all is quiet and no one is around. However, you must make sure that, like God in the quad, you are always about.

If it is in May or April, when the weather is not too cold, let her foal in a small clean paddock close to your house, free of implements lying around, or rusty iron. Let it have no banks or deep ditches. Mares creep off into a corner to give birth if they can. One foal dropped from the mother straight into a twelve-foot ditch and drowned. Another was born under a cart, and every time it tried to get up, knocked its head on the axle.

Only if it is early in the year (*must* you have an early foal?) and if it is cold, should you let your mare foal indoors. A loose box is no good – you want a big shed. But how can you properly disinfect a big shed (there is more chance of disease indoors)? You can of course build a special foaling-box and a sitting-up room for yourself, complete with closed-circuit television, so that you can watch her while you are eating supper. But you are not trying to supervise a dozen mares who may all produce Classic winners at any moment, and you do not send the second footman with your chauffeur to collect the fish and chips at frying time.

The snag about an outdoor foaling is the possibility of something going seriously wrong when it is too late to move the mare. You will then have to fix up some lighting – say, car headlights. But she will not appreciate being floodlit if all is proceeding smoothly.

Sit up and watch. You want to see her, but not to let her know you are there. If you can hear her eating, all is well. Go and have forty winks. But if you have forty-five, you might come out again to discover the foal is born. Cart-mares usually give birth easily and quickly, but you might find yourself in the middle of a crisis. However, if she is standing quietly, all right. If she is restless, she may be about to start, but again she may not. Dawn may come, and another day. She will now probably wait until nightfall, though there is no guarantee. Your stamina might be due for testing.

If you have no Trusty Adviser, or if he is a retired railway carter who has seen no more foalings than you have, your wife might co-operate, even though only to ring the vet lucidly as soon as you come rushing into the house, out of your wits because something is happening which you think is wrong. On the other hand, it might be much better if you exchanged roles. Swallow your pride if she is made of sterner stuff than you. Many wives are.

You will of course have had a discussion with your vet and he will have a rough idea when the mare is due to foal. If you have no Trusty Adviser, you may feel it is worth ringing the vet as soon as parturition begins, but it would be a good idea to make this a firm arrangement in advance.

Mares foal lying down, or should do. The first thing you will see protruding from the vulva is the water-bag, the outer membrane. This will burst and discharge fluid, perhaps a lot. The cast of the drama, all wrapped in the inner transparent membrane, in order of appearance from now on, is as follows: the front legs, with their little hooves pointing downwards and one somewhat in front of the other; the nose, followed by the whole head resting on the legs; the shoulders, which are the most difficult part and have to come out sideways because they are deep; finally, the rest of the foal, which should now slide out fairly easily.

The foal will probably break the bag himself, but you can slit it. For the first time in eleven months, he now has to start breathing. He is still joined to his mother by the umbilical cord, and it is important that nothing should be done to interfere with this for a little while. The sole means of maintaining life until breathing began, it is now busy acting as a pipe-line whereby the blood of the placenta is transfused into the new-born foal. He could scarcely be expected to survive unless he has this. After all, it is his, not his mother's, even though she made it for him.

When the mare recovers and gets up in her own good time, or when her precocious little offspring rises to his feet and starts to wobble his way about, the cord will break at its weakest point, just below his belly. Nature will immediately seal the fracture and, unless the conditions you provide are bad, prevent contamination, particularly from the dreaded foe known as navel or joint ill. But you can help by disinfecting the navel with iodine.

The placenta will still be hanging from the mare's vulva. Do not interfere with this, except perhaps to tie up the bottom of it so that it does not reach below her hocks if you think there may be any danger of her treading on it. In an hour or so, it will come away of its own accord. Keep it all most carefully and show it to your Trusty Adviser so that you can be absolutely certain that it has all come out, including the hippomane, a flat fleshy oval about six inches long, aptly nicknamed the 'false tongue' – a trophy formerly much prized as a magic aid to fertility but now recognised in more mundane fashion as a sort of dustbin of rubbish that the mare could not previously expel, as it was contained within the placenta. If the Trusty Adviser says the after-birth is not complete, or if you are not convinced that he is really sure, call the vet. Any retained within the mare will probably kill her.

If, at the birth, the members of the cast do not appear gracefully, you will need help. It may be necessary to pull on a leg because the shoulders are going to come too square and get stuck. There can be more serious difficulties, such as the head turned the wrong way round. But do not meddle in this situation yourself, unless there is no Trusty Adviser and your vet has rung to say with his last breath that he has just driven his car into a wall five miles back and his partner's house is on fire. Plenty of foals have been killed, and mares seriously damaged, by clumsy 'assistance' from people who do not know what they are doing.

Let the mother lick her foal. Should he be her first one, she may be astonished to see what has happened, or even frightened and reluctant to take to him. By smelling him, she will know that he is to do with her. If you have officiously rubbed him with towels because he is wet, or cleaned him up with carbolic soap or after-shave lotion, she will think he is something of yours.

Do not jump to the conclusion that his legs are deformed or broken. They are rubbery at first – otherwise he could not have come out into the world. Do not be afraid that the mare will tread on him: she will not, unless you get in the way yourself. Watch that she lets the foal suck. He will fall around in a most amusing or pathetic way, and try her in the most absurd places at first. Do not worry unless he has failed to get a drink after a couple of hours, in which case you should give some gentle assistance. Should the mare be unwilling to stand still, you must hold her, or tie her up, or lift a foreleg to keep her still. Once she has got the idea, all will be well.

The first milk, the colostrum, is of vital importance. The new-born foal has no resistance whatever against germs. The mother has built up in her own blood all the antibodies she needs for herself, but those she has stored for the foal are in her milk, not in the blood of the placenta. The foal is unable to benefit from the antibodies after, at the most, twenty-four hours. But, having had this early milk, the little animal develops immunity against whatever enemies the mother has had contact with during recent months, and these defences will last him until he has developed his own antibodies.

Let the foal come to you and make the first contact. He should find out for himself that you will not hurt him. Your mare may react strangely. Some dear gentle creatures that you can do anything with become so foal-proud the first day or two that they will even attack their friend and master. Do not be distraught at such odd behaviour. This sort make the best mothers.

## Covering after foaling

John Proe is a farmer who happens to keep cart-stallions. He is not a whole-time breeder of horses. There are no such places as heavy-horse stud farms. Therefore, it is highly unlikely that he will be prepared to receive a pregnant mare and supervise the birth, as in more elegant circles. If, then, your mare is in foal and you want to have her covered again after the birth, the foal will first be born at home. Compared with the barren or maiden mare which we have been thinking of so far, covering one with foal at foot presents a couple of special problems.

One of these difficulties is that of actually obtaining a successful mating. The matron's first heat is usually at its height on about the ninth day after foaling, though it may be a little earlier or later. After that, oestrus can be difficult to detect – or even entirely absent, perhaps because the production of milk inhibits ovulation. Therefore, it always used to be recommended that the mare should be covered at the 'foaling heat'. Furthermore, the chances of conception were thought to be best at that time.

However, it is now known that the likelihood of resorption of the resultant embryo, or of abortion, is very strong when conception takes place at this first heat. And some people would even dispute the second proposition, claiming that the conception-rate is then at its lowest, not its highest. Probably the age-old faith in the foaling heat is due to the fact that, in a busy summer on the farm, this was the only one that was really properly noticed.

Certainly, it is wise not to cover so soon if the mare has had a bad time in giving birth the week before, or if the new foal is her first. If you leave it until later, the possible disappointment of her not coming into oestrus at all can be overcome, if you wish, by an injection. Your predecessors had to accept the fact that, whereas some mares produced a foal annually without batting an eyelid, others had one only in alternate years.

The other problem, if a minor one, is the foal itself. If you intend to send your mare to Proe's, a long journey at the tender age of four or five days is a risky operation. You may be forced to wait until he is older. If, then, the mare proves slow to conceive, you will be without mother and child for longer than you would like – and with no certainty of success. We shall leave it at that. The decision is yours.

It may seem easier if the stallion is to be old Joe's. Leave the foal at home if you can, but that is possible only if you will soon be back. Make sure he is left in some place as strong as a prison cell and as safe as a padded one. When frightened, a horse, and especially a baby one, will do things that seem really silly to us, such as jumping through a window. A wall is a wall, but the glass in the window is daylight and freedom. So he tries to jump, with gory results. If you have another foal, or some other harmless animal to leave him with, so much the better. Two are always better than one. Company gives confidence, especially to a little creature waiting for its mother to come back.

But you will probably have to take the foal along, too. It might then be a good idea to park the lorry a mile away and leave the foal in it. (It might also be a good thing psychologically for the mare if she has to walk the last part.) He will squeal and holler when separated from her and, if she can hear him, she will not attend to the business on hand. Some mares have to be coaxed by the stallion before they are willing to receive him, and she must not be distracted.

The alternative, to allow the foal to be around at the time of covering, could be dangerous. He will be in the way. He may be under your feet just when you need to jump out of the way yourself. You will have a terrible job to hold the mare. And the horse is more likely to prance about if there is any such distraction. Stallions have been known to kick a foal dead, not out of malice but in their frenzy.

In days past, when stallions clumped their way round the country-side and could call on you or at the local pub, the system, though inefficient, at least obviated this difficulty. One famous Suffolk mare had sixteen outstanding foals in consecutive years and her owner had no problems. The covering was always done at home and the horse had gone as soon as his leader could finish his beer, because they both had dates at the village pub.

## Young life

Not a word here about the things that can go wrong in the first days and weeks of life. You must confide in your vet if you have any anxieties. But do not worry if the foal has some slight diarrhoea when the mother is on heat, for this sometimes affects the milk.

Entrancing as the new member of your ménage will be, do not try to play with him. Instead, put him on a little head collar after just a few days. He will think he is leading you about, though it is your belief you are leading him. You will both be happy, and you will be getting him used to being briefly separated from his mother. This will be useful if you want to take him to a show or two. But do not take him to too many. This first little lesson he will never forget, so make it a success. Never leave him with the head collar on, for he will get into all sorts of trouble with it, catching it on a hedge or post, or even getting a hind leg caught in it while trying to scratch himself.

Life will be good for him if he can drink and sleep and rush madly round in little circles in between times. But get him used to being handled, and even to having his feet picked up. He should learn not only to trust but to respect you. If you just play about with him, he will soon become unmanageable and, when he is bigger, dangerous.

In the hey-day of the cart-horse, the largest and most successful of stallion-owners every year bought scores of two-year-olds, of which a few matured to the perfection he sought. He made it a rule never to buy one which had been reared by a woman. This doctrine may seem ridiculous, but he believed vast experience had taught him that women were over-kind. Certainly, any spoiled young entire horse, requiring to learn a hard lesson about behaviour later on, will remain smoulderingly dangerous and resentful, however much he outwardly accepts new discipline. Hiring out stallions all over the country, this man had to see to it that they were not only good but dependable.

Right from the beginning, then, do not be 'soft' and do not make a practice of feeding the little animal tit-bits. He will begin to pester you, and may end up vicious.

The mother may be able to do a few light jobs very soon after foaling. On the other hand she might be poorly for a few weeks. Throughout the time she is nursing, she should not have long spells of work, because priority must be give to milk production. And the foal is a real tie. Shut him in a shed, and he shouts for her. On a small place, he is never out of earshot. You cannot even walk away and leave her to stand quietly, as you could before. She will make off, to see her foal – taking her cart, or whatever it is, with her. You therefore have to adapt your routine.

At six months, the foal must be weaned. His mother will suffer and begin to go back in condition if he is allowed to go on playing the baby and supplementing what he can easily now eat for himself by drinking her milk. One day, therefore, take him right away, away from sight and sound of her, a clean break. To try to do it gradually is useless. Give the foal some company – another foal, if there is one around, a pony, even a goat. But not a herd of Friesians. If you have no pony, borrow one. If you are short of space, persuade a neighbour to have the foal for a month or two.

It is no good putting him in an empty field on his own, and expecting him to be there when you next pay a visit. He will soon find a way through the hedge. Incidentally, if you can shut him in a shed for a while during this time, it is a good opportunity to break him to a halter. And begin a worming programme, as devised by the vet. Do not just give him some of mum's stuff.

What are your plans for him now? If you are going to sell him, do it quickly, as soon as he is weaned. It is pointless to delay – financially, emotionally, and practically.

Some people claim that they could not possibly sell a foal 'except to a good home'. You might indeed find one, but in a few months he might move on again, perhaps to a bad home. And the man whom you sold him to cheaply has made a nice profit. If you are like that, do not breed horses, and save yourself the tears. There was once a man who had a mare and an acre. He bred from her and she did well. After five years he had five horses. The first foal was his wife's darling, the second he liked himself, the third was just too sweet, and the last was only a baby. Chaos, disease and bankruptcy stared him in the face.

Keep the foal by all means if you have the accommodation – provided its quality and its sex fit in with your plans. It is foolish to keep a colt foal if breeding is still your main aim. But if you wanted a gelding without buying one, that is fine. He will be a gelding, when you have had him castrated.

Castration is best left until he is a yearling, and should be done in the autumn. He will then be eighteen months old, or thereabouts. By that time he will have gained a little presence and his neck will have a bit of shape, whereas if it is done earlier he will look mare-ish. It can also be done in the spring when he is two. But the summer, when flies are about, is certainly the wrong time.

There are several methods of castration but, as you are not going to do it (the law says so), the vet will do it his preferred way. You must not dictate, but you will have to give unskilled assistance. He may put the colt 'out' with one injection and bring him round again with another. If you cannot bear to watch, get your Trusty Adviser (or anyone sensible) and go indoors to watch telly. There was once a whole family which was very good at milking cows and other jobs on their farm, but whenever blood began to flow they all fainted. If you are that sort, you will only get in the way of an operation which might be called (infelicitously) child's play for the vet.

Your colt will drip blood for a few hours afterwards, but there should be no real bleeding. If there is, he will bleed to death, so keep an eye on him. Infection could also set in, but your vet will guard against it. Though he is bound to go back in condition, it will not be long before he begins to thrive again. Obviously, the colt cut in spring might not do so well at early shows as he would if the operation had been done the previous autumn.

Do not expect him to respond to his sudden change of status by an immediate alteration in his attitude to life. At the age of eighteen months, he will not only have been old enough to take an interest in mares but, if allowed to do so, could have fathered a foal himself. One celebrated Clydesdale was the product of a childish union, due to a groom's slackness, between a couple whose combined ages were thirty-five months. It will be months before the gelded animal completely ceases behaving as if he were entire, even though, never having served a mare, he does not understand what he has missed.

The only excuse for delaying castration is the belief that the colt will make a stallion. What if you think yours will? You could advertise him, and see what the experts think. Do this when he is a yearling and then, if no one wants him, cut him in the autumn. (Someone might have snapped him up – to make him into a good gelding!)

The longer castration is delayed, the more serious it is, and the longer the horse will take to regain health and spirits. And it must be remembered that, as soon as an entire colt is two years old, he has to take the Ministry test and possess a licence. Furthermore, if he is eligible for a stud-book, it may be necessary to register him in that, or at least record his birth and parentage, at a very tender age. But that is a pointless waste of money if he is definitely due to join 'the great majority'.

An uncut colt rising two will never be kept in by a few fences if he can sense mares about. Unless you make absolutely sure he cannot get out, he will do so. If your neighbour breeds Arabs, he will not be pleased to find your animal amongst his mares in the morning. Mrs Featherstonehaugh will be outraged if she looks out of the window at breakfast to see your wretched cart colt serving her hunter mare. This sort of thing leads to broken friendships.

From eighteen months, your filly or young gelding should be

197

allowed to grow on until you can begin breaking and training. But, from the earliest days, you should have been teaching the elements of correct behaviour so that you can lead and box your animal and make him or her stand properly, on all four legs. And you should have always been watching the feet. Are they wearing too slow, or too fast?

Do not feed too much. Soft bones are easily and quickly produced. Good hard bones grow slower. 'Soon ripe, soon rotten' used to be the saying, and it still applies.

## Stick to your plans

Even if things go wrong in the early years, continue to breed to a purpose. Provided your goal has been sensibly selected in the first place, do not be deflected by setbacks. Stick to the type you are aiming at, as near as you can. You will never get anywhere by chopping and changing. Dithering about, accepting conflicting advice at alternate turns, you will end with worse than you started with. By keeping to a plan, you will, in the end and if you deserve it, get some way along the narrow road you had originally mapped out.

Our final word must be one of caution. This book is a little elementary primer and no more. You will build up your knowledge by personal contact with experienced people. You may even go on a short course of instruction. But you will not be an expert. Many people delude themselves that they are, pontificating upon matters of which, until recently, they were ignorant and using expressions by which the old-stager can recognise the source of their information.

Be a listener, not a talker. An old groom who worked many years for one of the most prosperous men in the whole cart-horse business was once asked to account for his employer's phenomenal success. The questioner expected to hear some gem of wisdom. And he did, for the answer was 'He was a man who always kept his ears open, and his mouth shut.'

The wisdom of the horsemen was never to be found in books, and only its rudiments can even now be learned from them. Passed from one generation to another, it became ever more profound as the experience of the sons was added to the tradition of their fathers. For twenty years, as the work-horse seemed to draw near to the point of extinction, this vast store of deep understanding remained intact in a dwindling number of families. The newcomer, unaware even of the existence of what he does not know about the relationship of man and working horse, should approach with humility.

# Postscript

A few horses drop dead. But not many. Mostly, they just grow older and feebler, like us. Or they contract some disease which is ultimately fatal, as we might. Or they become afflicted by one of the infirmities associated with advanced age and which make their lives a misery – they are rheumatic, their teeth are worn out, or their legs are gone.

For *Homo sapiens*, euthanasia has not been approved. The seemingly incurable disease may, through a miracle of science or faith, be cured after all. And toothless and rheumatic Grandma, whose legs have gone, might have other compensations to make life worth living. But the paramount argument against anyone signing the death-warrant of someone else must remain religious or moral – even though the achievements of medicine have confused the issue by pushing the hurdle of mortality farther back than it was originally placed by nature (or God), with the result that the preservation of life sometimes becomes the prevention of death, which is not the same.

Your horse's only pleasures derive from health. When he is too old or too incurably sick to be happy, you have none of the anguish associated with human suffering. If you have any humanity in you, you will send him for slaughter, as our God-fearing ancestors did. The Victorians were sentimental. Up and down the country, there are graves of many a cart stallion, sadly missed by a loving owner who, in token of the valuable service fees he had earnt, set up a memorial tablet with home-spun verses carved upon it. But who was it who had ordered the horse to be shot? The owner himself, and quite right, too.

Do not therefore donate your aged horse to a home of rest. Have no dealings, in any way at all, with any of these. The whole concept is wrong. A charity which aims to prevent cruelty to any animal, or which tries to repair physical damage caused by the mindless selfishness of man, such as the cleaning of oil from a sea-bird's plumage, is a different matter. But in a home of rest, however well run, a horse cannot be restored to joy and vigour and may even suffer unnecessarily simply by being kept alive.

We are here dealing with a principle, and in no way wish to cast doubt upon the good intentions or the integrity of those who run such geriatric establishments today. In the past, there may have been those who took advantage of the curious propensity of many affluent people to shower money upon any organisation which claimed to champion the cause of old horses, or of horses which might suffer later unless protected now. How the income of some societies was spent was often a confusing matter. And in the future, new ways may be discovered for channelling misdirected charity into ingenious schemes. A benefactor invited to adopt a horse might not know that Dobbin, his protégé of yesterday, has to be slaughtered today to pay the hay-bill for the others, and will be unobtrusively replaced by a new Dobbin tomorrow. A second sympathiser might be invited to buy a plot of ground for the burial of a horse but never have proof of any obsequies. But these speculations about the future, like the fiddles of the past, are by the way. Slaughter, not a home of rest, is what must happen at the last, because it is humane, whereas in the waiting for death there is no true compassion at all.

There are two types of slaughter-house. The local knacker-man will give you a trifling sum. For a 'stinker', nothing. To his place go corpses found in fields, animals suffering from dread diseases and emaciated meatless creatures. Of the second sort, there are a few only, scattered strategically round the country. These are licensed to slaughter for the meat trade and the horses that come their way are, when dead, mostly exported. To some people, but not the British (which puzzles the non-British), horse flesh is an acceptable meat. It stands to reason, therefore, that you will be paid a large sum for a horse that you send to one of these places. Prices fluctuate considerably for all sorts of reasons, some of them intelligible only to those who understand the Common Market, but they represent real money.

Since heavy horses grow good meat on them quicker than cattle do, there is in fact a strong case for an ambitious beef-grower to switch to horses. He might make a good thing out of it. On the other hand, he might find the price has dropped just when he is ready to sell, as happens to so many in various branches of farming. Actually, anyone contemplating this way of making a living would be advised to specialise in good plump cobs. They make the best prices per pound, since cart-horses have a bigger proportion of bone. Your money, by the way, is calculated on dead-weight, which means that you will get less than you might have hoped.

Do not be too disgusted by all this. In all the company of cart-horse breeders in this country, we cannot think of anyone who has taken up, like their Continental counterparts, the production of horses for meat. They would not fancy the idea. But they cannot afford to be silly. When they produce an animal that turns out, in spite of the most excellent pedigree, to be almost worthless, or when an animal becomes worthless through injury, they are forced for economic reasons to use the licensed meat-trade. In this way, the misfits and disasters actually support, not jeopardise, the whole breeding enterprise. Without such a rewarding insurance against disappointment or accident, it is doubtful whether the heavy breeds would have survived the dark ages of the Fifties and Sixties, or would still survive now. So we must be thankful. And you, for your part, must be a man with more money than sense if you refuse to let Captain and Dolly serve you in death as they did in life.

If you do not relish having anything to do with death, persuade someone who has regular dealings with one of these regional licensed premises to organise the whole thing for you. For a suitable cut off the joint, such a kind friend will come and collect your horse – if you wish, when you are out for the day. He can even arrange personally to watch that all happened as it should, and bring you back the consoling news, with your cheque.

By the way, it is nonsense to say, as someone might tell you, that horses have premonitions about their fate, that 'they know what is going to happen'. One moment they are alive and behaving normally: a second later, dead, without ever knowing that anything even struck them. Not a bad way of ending the journey – for your horse, or for you.

# Further Reading and Information

Amid the welter of books about horses, the only one devoted to the care and management of the heavy breeds has been written by the founder and editor of the American *Draft Horse Journal*:

Maurice Telleen, *The Draft Horse Primer, A Guide to the Care and Use of Work Horses and Mules* (Rodale Press, Emmaus, Pa, 1977).

The authoritative work on the history and varieties of harness is: Terry Keegan, *The Heavy Horse, Its Harness and Harness Decoration* (Pelham Books Ltd, 1973).

For veterinary information, we suggest: The TV Vet, *The TV Vet Horse Book* (The Farming Press Ltd, 3rd edition revised, 1974); Dr Alistair Fraser and Dr Frank Manolson, *Fraser's Horse Book* (Pitman Publishing Ltd, 1979).

Those interested in the history of cart horses could read: Keith Chivers, *The Shire Horse* (J. A. Allen and Co Ltd, 1976, reprinted 1980). This enormously long work, which studies also the development of the other breeds, appears in abbreviated form (and without the study of bloodlines and the numerous appendices) in a paperback under the same title (Futura Books, 1978) at about one-fifth the size.

Three journals are wholly or partly devoted to heavy horses: *Horse and Driving*, bi-monthly (Watmoughs Ltd, Idle, Bradford BD10 8NL); a regular order with your newsagent or a postal subscription is advisable. *The Heavy Horse*, quarterly (Woodside House, Pembury, Kent, TN2 4BG); postal subscriptions only. *The Draft Horse Journal*, quarterly (Route 3, Waverley, Iowa).

For other information about current and future events, join the breed society of your choice. Write to the appropriate secretary of:

British Percheron Horse Society: D. G. Maskell, Owen Webb House, Gresham Road, Cambridge, CB1 2ER.

Clydesdale Horse Society: John Fraser, 22 Argyle Terrace, Dunblane, Perthshire.

Shire Horse Society: Roy W. Bird MBE, East of England Showground, Peterborough, PE2 0XE.

Suffolk Horse Society: P. Ryder-Davies, 6 Church Street, Woodbridge, Suffolk, IP12 1DH.

# Index

Items of harness and equipment are, where possible, listed just once. For example, 'ridger' and 'tug' occur frequently in the text, but your only purpose in looking up the words would be to see what these things are or do.

References to photographs (in **bold** type) are generally given only for words actually mentioned in the captions. The picture on page 128 is indexed only under 'Show harness', but by looking at it you can identify the separate items. For 'Plough harness' the index refers you only to 122, but horses are wearing this sort of harness in eight other pictures, too. Similarly, for 'Shire horses' you are invited to look at 10 and 126, but most of the pictures happen to show this breed.

Amanda Smith-Jones, Granny, Alfie, the Scrubbins, Mrs Featherstonehaugh, and even Proe and Bloggs, do not appear here, but your Trusty Adviser does; he must not remain a figment of the imagination.

The references to 'Safety', dauntingly numerous, cannot be complete, for the theme is implicit throughout the text — as is 'Patience', which has but two entries here. Poor manners, alluded to several times, are omitted from the index. It is only The Other Fellow who needs to consult that point, and it would not occur to him to do so.

Abortion, 180, 188, 193
Acorns, 39
Adders, 39
Adnams' and Co Ltd, Percherons, **14-15**
Advice: buying, 28; ploughing matches, 168, 169-70, 171; shows, 159; *see also* Trusty Adviser
Age: first horse, 20; how reckoned, 181; old age, 199; working life, 13
Agricultural turn-outs, 162-3, 166-7, **164-5**
Amateur owners, 17-18
Anaemia, 71
Andrews', Mrs Sheilagh, Suffolks, **19**
Antibodies, 192
Appetite, loss of, 74
Apple, 54
Ardennes horses, 24
Arthritis, 78
Assistance, week-ends, 28
Assistant, breaking and training, 134-6, 138, **137, 144**; learning to drive, 121; ploughing matches, 167, 168; hitching

to pole, 127; shows, 152; workings, 173-4
Attendant, turn-out classes, 162-3
Auction sales, 29-32

Back-band: plough harness, 122; trace, 120
Back-chain, 112
Backing into shafts, 116; teaching, 138, **139**
Backing vehicle, 78; teaching, 138; *see also* Breeching
Badekins, 123
Bag for grooming kit, 63
'Bag up' before foaling, 189
Bandages, 77
Barley, 53
Barley straw, 55
Barrow, stable, 56
Bars: of foot, 80; of mouth, 107
Bass, 149, **148**
Battekins, 123
Baulk, 123
Bay coat: breeds, 25-6; true and hybrid, 178
Beam, 123
Beans, 53

Bearing-rein, 109-10
Bedding, 55-6
Beet, sugar, 53
Bells, 129
Belly band: shaft harness, 112, 113; trace, 120
Binder, 98
Birth, *see* Foaling
Bit-ring, 107, 109
Bit-strap, 107
Biting, 67
Bits, 107-8, **108**; breaking (mouthing), 134, **134**
Black coat: breeds, 25-6, 29; true and hybrid, 178
Blinkers, 106-7
Blood testing (pregnancy), 188
Bodkins, 123
Body brush, 59, 63, **58**
Bog spavin, 78
Bolt, 123
Bone spavin, 78
Bot-destroyer, 73
Bot-fly, 72-3; colic, 76
Bot-knife, 73
Bowel, blockage of, 76
Bracken, 39
Brake, 118; *see also* Breeching

Bran, 52
Brasses, 127
Breaking and training, 64; first steps, 133-7, **134, 137, 139**; loading up, **144, 145**; on the road, 142-3, **143**; shaft work, 138, 140-1
Breaking harness, **134**
Breast-strap, 128
Breech-band, 114
Breeching: pole harness, 126; shaft, 112, 114, **113**
Breeching-chains, 114
Breed societies: addresses, 202; advice on insurance, 48; stallions available, 178-9; *see also* Stud-book
Breeding: buying a mare for, 18-20, 21-2, 23; from covering to foaling, 176-94
Breeds, 23-4, 25-6; *see also* Clydesdale; Percheron; Shire; Suffolk horses
Brewer's grains, 54
Brewery horses, 12, 13, **14-15, 126**; feeding, 49-50
Bridge of saddle, 112
Bridle, 106-7; leaving on, 131
British Percheron Horse Society, 202
British Percheron horses, *see* Percheron horses
Brow-band, 107
Brown coat: breeds, 25-6; true and hybrid, 178
Brush: stable, 56; grooming, 58-9, 63; *see also* Body brush; Dandy brush; Water brush
Brushes on harness, 129
Bucket: feed and water, 55; washing, 63
Buckles: fastening, 117; matching, 127; quality, 130
Bulbs of heel, 80
Buying a horse, 28-36; auction, 29-32; dealer, 34-5; private purchase, 32-4; through someone else, 35-6

Cannon bone, 78
Cap (cape), 128
Carnivals, 174
Carrot, 54
Cart harness, *see* Shaft harness
Cartilages, 78
Carting jobs, 85-6
Carts, 87-92, **88, 89, 90, 91, 93**; backing, 118; climbing into, 131-2, **132, 133**; on hills, 118; transporting, 44
Castration, 196-7; intelligence and, 65
Cauldwell, Miss Jenny, **163**
Chaff, 52
Chaff-cutter, 55

Chain harness, *see* Plough harness
Chains, cleaning, 127
Cheek-strap, 106-7
Chemical beauty-aids, 57
Ches(t)nut coat: breeds, 25-6; inherited, 178
Chock (chog), 99, **41**
Choosing horse, 18-26
Clipper, 63; electric, 62
Clipping, 60, 62
Cloths, grooming, 63
Clydesdale Horse Society, 202
Clydesdale horses, 23-4, **10**; auction sales, 29; colour, 25, 26, 178; crossed with Shires, 22
Coat, staring, 74, 75
Coffin bone, 78
Colds, 75
Colic, 76; bot-fly, 72; worms, 71
Collar, 100, 106; fitting, **103, 104, 105**; measuring, **102**; spare, 130
Collar-straps, 126
Colostrum, 192
Colour (horses): breeds, 24-6, 29; heredity, 178
Colour (implements), 95
Colour (vehicles), 90
Colours for plaiting, 147, 149
Colts: *see* Castration; Stallion licence; Yearlings
Comb, *see* Curry comb; Mane comb
Commands, 67-8, 108; teaching, 135
Commerce, *see* Towns
Commercial turn-outs, 162-3, 166-7
Communication, 66-70; oral, 67-8, 108; touch, 66-7; visual, 68-70
Conception, 179-80; best month for, 182; correct time to achieve, 181, 184, 185, 186; in foaling heat, 193
Contagion at mating, 187
Corn-bin, 55
Cornish decorated harness, 129, **129**
Corpus luteum, 188
Cost of horsepower: farms, 9; towns, 12-13
Cotton wool, 77
Cough, 75
Coupling, 122, 123
Cracked heels, 63
Crib-biting, 31
Cross-breds, 22
Crupper: plough harness, 122; shaft, 114; trace, 120
Cultivators, 96
Curb, 78
Curry comb, 59, 63, **58**

Cuts, powder for, 77

Dandruff, 57
Dandy brush, 59, 63, **58**
Deadly nightshade, 39
Dealers, 34-5
Death, 199-201
Decorated harness, 129; at shows, 160, **129**
Dettol, 76, 77
Diarrhoea in foals, 194
Digestive system, 50, 52, 76
Dipper, 55
Discipline, 64, 65, 66; foals, 195; tit-bits, 40
Disease, contagious, at mating, 187
Diseases, hereditary, 177; foot and leg, 78; shivering, 30
Donkeys, worms in, 72
Drag shoe, 118
Drain in stable, 56
Draught-bar, 122-3
Dress at shows, 153-4, 161, 162-3
Drill, 96
Drilling corn, **171**
Driving-reins, 108-9, 112, 114-15, **113**; Pair-horse, 126
Drug bat, 118
Drugs, disposal of, 77
Dung: clearing out, 55; healthy horse, 74; quantity, 76; worms, 72
Dung-cart, 89, **88**
Dung-heap, 56
Dung-spreader, *see* Manure-spreader

Ear-caps, **87**
Ears: cold, 74; communicating by, 69
Egg, egg-cells, 179-80, 181, 182
Electric clipper, 62
Electric groomer, 60, 62, 63, **61**
Embryo: abortion of, 180, 188, 193; resorption of, 188, 193
Emotions, equine, expression of, 65, 66-7, 68, 69-70; human, 65
Equine metritis, 187
Eyes: as communicators, 69-70; dull, 74
Eyesight, 69

Face-piece, 128
Fallopian tube, 179-80
'False tongue', 191
Fan, 128
Farm horses, arguments for, 9-11
Farm work, 85-7
Farrier, 80-2
Feeding, 49-55; causing colic, 76; finicky, 76; pregnant mares, 189; tit-bits, 40; young animals, 137, 198

Fences, 36-8
Fertiliser-spreader, 92, **97**
Fertiliser-spreading, 86
Fertilising paddocks, 39
Fêtes, 174
Fetlock, 78
Fever in feet, 83
Flies, 72-3
Flights, 149, **148**
Float, 89
Fly head terrets, 129
Fly-sheet, 153
Fly-spray, 77
Foal: dam being mated again, 193-4; first six months, 194-5; handling, 192; sale of, 195; showing, 159; weaning, 195-6; worming, 196
Foaling, 189-92; best month for, 182
Foaling heat, 193
Follicle, 180, 182, 188
Foot, 77, 78, 80-4, **79**; cleaning, 82; examining, 60, 82
Force-chain, 118
Fork, stable, 56
Founder, 83
Foxglove, 39
Frisian mare, 24
Frog, 80, 81, 82, 83
Funerals, 174-5, **173**
Furrow horse, 123

Galls, 77
Gasterophiles, 72
Gates, safety, 38, 39, 131
Gateway, negotiating, 118
Geld, *see* Castration
Gelding as first horse, 18-20, 21-3
Genetics of coat colour, 178
George V, King, 176
Gestation, 189
Girth-strap, 114
G O gears, 121
Grade horses, 21
'Grapes', 83
Grass: over-heated, 40; pasture, 38, 49
Grease: disease on leg, 63, 83; healthy, 59
Grey coat: breeds, 25-6; inherited, 178; stains on, 62
Groomer, electric, 60, 62, 63, **61**
Grooming, 57-63; for show, 62-3
Grooming kit, **58**
Gut, perforated, 72; ruptured, 71

Hair, pulling, 60
Halter, 99-100, **41, 101**
Hame-crook, 106
Hame-ring, 114
Hames, 100, 106

Hames-strap, 106, 128
Harness, 99-130; breaking, 134, **134**; bridle, bit and reins, 106-10; care of, 130; clean for shows, 160; collar and hames, 100, 106; decorated, 129, **129**; decorating, 127-9; halter, 99-100; plough, 121-3, **122**; pole, 123, 126-9, **126**; removal after work, 59; safe, 133, 135; shaft, 112, 114-17, **113**; show, 127-9, **128**; storage, 42; trace, 119-20, **119**
Harness classes, 160-1
Harnessing: *see* under types of harness above
Harrow, 96
Harrowing, 86, **10, 93**
Hay, 51-2; as chaff, 52; from paddocks, 38
Hay loader, 97
Hay-net, 55
Hay-prong, 56
Hay-rack, 55, **41, 43**
Hay-rake, 97, **87**
Hay-raking, 86, **87**
Hay sweep, 97
Hay-turner, 92, 97, **97**
Hay wisp, 59
Head collar, 99
Head held down, 74
Head-strap, 107
Health: general, 70-7; leg and foot, 77-84; *see also* Bedding; Feeding; Grooming; Neglect
Heat (mare), 180-1; foaling heat, 193; induced by injection, 187, 188, 193; 'silent', 188
Hedges, 36
Heels, cracked or greasy, 63
Help, *see* Advice; Assistance; Assistant, Trusty Adviser
Heredity: characteristics, 22, 23; coat colour, 178; influence of stallion, 177; unsoundness, *see* Diseases, hereditary
Hernia, strangulated, 76
Hills, going up and down, 118
Hippomane, 191
Hip-strap: shaft harness, 114; trace, 120
Hiring societies, 178-9
Hitch cart, 90, 92, **91, 93**
Hitching: *see* under Plough harness; Pole harness; Shutting-in; Trace harness
'Hobby' horses, 12, 17-18, 92
Hock, 78
Hoe, 96
Homes of Rest, 199-200
Hood, 128
Hoof, *see* Foot
Hoof oil, 63, 83-4

Hoof pick, 63, 82, **58**
Horn (wall) of foot, 80, 81, 82, 83
Horse cubes, 53
Horse flesh, 200-1
Horse-fly, 72
Horse societies, 179; *see also* Breed societies; Hiring societies
Hose-pipe: for legs, 82; in stable, 56
Housen, 128
Housing, 40-4

Implements, 92-8; safety, 132-3; transporting, 44
Indigestion, *see* Colic
Industry, *see* Towns
Influenza, 75
In-hand classes, 156-9
Injections: inducing heat, 187, 188, 193; on vet's instructions, 75
Insemination, 176
Insurance, 13, 46-8
Intelligence, 10, 65-6, 140-1; sixth sense, 69, 70
Intestines, damage to, 76
Iodine, 77

Joint ill, 191
Joints, 78
Judges: first impressions of, 156; harness classes, 161; in-hand classes, 156-9; ploughing matches, 171; turn-out classes, 163, 166

Kay, David, 16
Kicking, 67
Knee, 78
Knub, 128

Lameness, 78, 82-3
Laminitis, 83
Lancashire decorated harness, 129
Land, 36-40
Land horse, 123
Law: castration, 196; colts uncastrated, 197; insurance, 46, 47; stallion-licensing, 176; straying horses, 37; transporting horses, 44, 46; *see also* Warranty
Leading-rein, 110, 115; show harness, 128; trace, 120
Leather: care of, 130; extra for show, 128; sweating horse, 123
Leg, 77-8, 82-3; lump on, 28; washing, 63
Licence for stallions, 176-7; at two years, 197
Ligaments, 78

Lines, 109, 123, **122**; shortening, **110, 111**
Linseed, 53
Listlessness, 74
Liverpool bit, 107-8
Loading-up, 144-6, **144, 145**
Local show society, 179
Log in training, 136, **137**
Loin-strap, 114
Long gears, 119
Loose box, 42, 44, **43**
Lorry, *see* Motor lorry
Lung-worms, 72

Maize, 53
Mane: grooming, 60; plaiting, 147, 149
Mane comb, 60, 63, **58**
Manger, 55, **41, 43**
Mangold, 54
Manure, horse, 55
Manure-heap, 56
Manure-spreader, 92, 96-7, **96**
Mare: as first horse, 18-20, 21-3; away to stud, 185-7; condition for service, 183; covered after foaling, 193-4; covered by local horse, 183-5; foaling, 189-92; mating, correct time for, 181, 184, 185, 186; pregnancy, 188-9; sexual cycle, 179-82, 186; 'trying', 183-4; with foal (shows), 159; with foal (work etc), 195
Martingale, 128
Mash, 52
Medicines, over-use of, 39
Meeter-straps, 114
Memory, 10, 65
Metritis, 187
Midlands Shire Foal Show and Sale, 29
Milk: first, 192; mare in heat, 193, 194
Mineral lick, 51
Misrepresentation Act (1967), 34
Motor lorry: cost of, in towns, 12-13; to transport animals, *see* Transporting horses
Mower, 92, 97, **97**

Name: choice of, 67; use of, 135
Navel ill, 191
Navicular bone, 78
Navicular disease, 78
Neck-straps, 128
Neck-yoke, 123
Neglect, 17, 70; effect on intelligence, 65
Nondescript horses, 23
Nose-band, 107

Oat straw, 52

Oats, 52
Oestrus, *see* Heat
Oil glands, 57, 62
Old age, 18, 199
Oral communication, 67-8
Ovaries, 179, 188
Ovulation, 179, 181, 182; double, 180

Pad: cart saddle, 112; pole harness, 126
Paddocks: divided land, 36; fencing, 36-8; maintenance, 38-9, 49; pasture, 38, 49; worms in, 73
Paraffin: cleaning legs, 63; shining coats, 153
Parasites: harboured on land, 36; on skin, 57-8; *see also* Flies; Worms
Pastern, 78, 80, 81; grease, 83
Pasture, *see* Paddocks
Patience: loading up, 145; training, 137-40
Peas, 53
Peat moss, 55, 56
Pedal bone, 78, 80
Pedigree, 21-3; stallions, 177-8
Penis, 184
Perception, non-visual, 69, 70
Percheron Horse Society (British), 202
Percheron horses, 23-4, **14-15, 171**; colour, 26, 178; private sale, 29
Peritonitis, 72
Personality of horses, 70
Piebald coat, 25
Pin worms, 72
Placenta, 191, 192
Plaiting, 147-50; mane, **148**; tail, **150**
Plough, 96; transporting, 44, 45
Plough-band, 122
Plough harness, 121-3, **122**
Ploughing, 86, **124-5**; matches, 167-71, **169**
Pneumonia, 75
Poisons, 39; linseed, 53
Poland, implements from, 92, **97**
Pole harness, 123, 126-7, **126**
Pole-straps, 126
Potato bulker, 98
Pregnancy, 188-9; testing, 188; treatment during, 189
Premiums for stallions, 177
Prepotency, stallions, 177
Publicity from horses, 12, 17; at shows, 17, 162
Punishment, 66

'Quick' of foot, 80

Raffia, 149

Ragwort, 39
Railway sleeper, 136, **137**
Rake, 97, **97**
Rayner, Nick, horses, **169, 173** and others
Rein-guides, 120
Rein hanger, 128
Reins: *see* Bearing-rein; Driving-reins, Leading-rein
Resorption of embryo, 188, 193
Ribbon for plaiting, 149, **150**
Ridger, 112
Ringbone, 78
Rings: bit-rings, 107, 109; for lines, 109, 123; for reins, 109, 114
Roads: adjoining paddocks, 39-40; horses straying on, 37-8; preparing horses for, 135, **143**; training horses on, 142-3
Roan coat, 25-6; inherited, 178
Roller, 96, **94-5**
Roller-scotch, 118
Rope: halters, 99; lines and reins, 109
Roundworms, 71-2, 73
Rubber, stable, 62, 63, **58**
Rye straw, 149

Saddle: pole harness, 126; shaft, 112, 114
Saddle ring, 114
Safety: breaking and training, 133-41; bridle left on, 131; carnivals and fêtes, 174; climbing in cart, 131-2, **132, 133**; driving-reins, 109, 131; fencing, 36-8; fertilisers, 39; foot, 131; funerals, 175; gates, 38, 131; halter, **101**; handling horse, 67; harness, 133, 135; hitching to pole, 127; implements, 132-3; leading rein, 115; lines, 109, **110, 111**; medicines, 39; poisons, 39; roads, 142-3; runaways, 136, 138, 140; sand in water, 31; shafts, 131, 132, 133; shows, 151, 152, 167; shutting in, 112, 113; stabling, 44; strangers on land, 37-8, 39-40; straying horses, 37-8; traces, **121**; transporting horses, 44-5, 46; weed-killers, 39; wheels, 131-2; workings, 174; young horses together, 133
Sale, conditions of, 30
Sales, auction, 29-32
Salt, 51, 52
Salt-lick, 52, **41**
Sand, 40
Sandcrack, 82
Saunders', W.C., Suffolk team, **163**

Scales, 55
Scotch cart, 89, **89**
Scotland, clean harness, 160
Scottish decorated harness, 128, 129
Scurf, 57, 59
Season (mare), *see* Heat
Seat worms, 72
Semen, 180
Sex of first horse, 18-20
Shaft harness, 112, 114-15, **113**; for harness classes, 160
Shaft-horse, 112
Shaft-work, training for, 138, 140-1
Shafts: backing into, teaching, 138, **139**; dangers, 131, 132, 133; height of, 112, **113**
Shampoo, 62-3
Shavings, 56
Shavings-prong, 56
Shelter in paddocks, 40
Shire horses, 21, 23-4, **10, 126** and others; auction sales, 29; colour, 25, 29, 178; crossed with Clydesdales, 22
Shire Horse Show, 22
Shire Horse Society, 16; address, 202
Shire-type horses, 22; colour, 25; *see also* Shire horses
Shiverer, 118
Shivering, 30
Shoes, 80-2, 84; bevelled, 81-2; fullered, 81
Shovel, 56
Show, day of, 153-4, 156
Show harness, 127-9, **128**
Showground, arrival at, 154
'Showing' (mare in heat), 180
Shows: condition for, 152; different breeds at, 24; dress at, 153-4, 161, 162-3; foal classes, 159; harness classes, 160-1; in-hand classes, 156-9; practising for, 151-2; publicity from, 17, 162; qualifications for, 21, 22; safety, 151, 152, 167; transport to, 44-6, 153; turn-out classes, 162-3, 166-7
Shutting-in, 112, 115-17, **113**
Shutting-out, 118-19
Sickness, symptoms of, 74-5; *see also* Health
Side-straps, 128
Sidebone, 78
Silage, 53
Sinker, 99
Skewbald coat, 25
Skid-pan, 118
Skin, healthy, 74
Slaughter, 199-201; insurance, 47
Slaughter-houses, 200
Slurry cart, 96, **90**

Soap, soft, 62-3
Societies, *see* Breed societies; Hiring societies; Horse societies; Local show society
Sole, 80, 81, 82
Soundness, *see* Unsoundness; Warranty
Southern Counties Heavy Horse Association, 174
Spavin, 78
Sperm, 179, 180
Splint, 78, 82
Splint bones, 78
Sponge, grooming, 60, 63, **58**
Spreader, 120, **119**
Spreader-straps, 120, **119**
Stabling, 40-4
Staff: farms, 11; towns, 13, 16; *see also* Assistance; Assistant
Staling, *see* Urinating
Stall, 42, **41**
Stallion: choice of, 176-7, 182-3; location of, 23-4, 178-9; premium, 177
Stallion licence, 176-7; required at two years, 197
Standards (plaiting), 149
Stifle, 78
Stomach, ruptured, 76
Storage space, 42
Straw: bedding, 55; feeding, 52; plaiting, 149
Striking, 67
String harness, 119
Strongyles, 71
Stud-book: qualifications for, 21, 22; stallions in, 177, 178; young animals, **197**
Studs on straps, 127
Suffolk, standard of dress, 154
Suffolk Horse Society, 202
Suffolk horses, 23-4, **19, 163**; colour, 26, 178; private sale, 29
Sugar beet, 53
Sweat, 57, 59, 60, 62; too much harness, 123
Sweat glands, 57, 76
Swingle-trees, 122-3

Tack room, 42
Tail: grooming, 60; plaiting, 147, 149
Tail loop (tail ring), 149, **150**
Talking to horses, 68, 70, 135, 136
Tandem, 119
Tapeworms, 72
Taxation, 13
Temperature, 74, 75; laminitis, 83
Tendons, 78
Thermometer, 74
Threadworms, 72
Throat-lash, 107

Throat-strap, 107
Thrush, 82
Thwaites', Daniel and Co Ltd, Shires, 12-13, **126**
Tie-backs, 123, **124-5**
Tie-ring in stable, **41, 43**
Touch in communication, 66-7
Towelling, 60
Towns, horses working in, 12-16, **14-15, 126**
Trace-clipping, 60, 62
Trace harness, 119-20, **119**; at ploughing matches, 123
Trace horse, 119, 120; learning to drive, 120-1
Traces, 120; drop-link, **122**; plough harness, 122-3; pole harness, 126; slack in, **121**
Trade Descriptions Act (1968), 34
Traffic, *see* Roads
Training, *see* Breaking and training
Transporting horses, 42-6; good driving, 153; loading up, 144-6, **144, 145**
Transporting mare to stud, 186; with foal, 193
Transport of Animals Act, 46
Tree of saddle, 112, 114
Trolley, 87-8
Trusty Adviser, 27-8; breaking and training, 134, 140; buying a horse, 29, 33; castration, 196; farm work, 86-7; feeding, 54; at foaling, 191-2; plaiting up, 147; showing horse, 159; sickness, 75; stables, 44
'Trying' mare, 183-4
Tug (tug-chain), 106, 112, **113**
Turn-out, agricultural, **164-5**
Turn-out classes, 162-3, 166-7; at ploughing matches, 170
Twins, 180
Tyres, 88, 90, **88**

Umbilical cord, 191
Unfamiliar sights, 69
Unsoundness: foot, 81, 82, 83; hereditary, 78, 177; leg, 78; shivering, 30; *see also* Warranty
Urinating: difficulty in (colic), 76; mares, 180; return to stable, 56
Urine: healthy horse, 74; quantity, 76
Urine samples (pregnancy), 188
Uterus, 179

Vehicles, horse-drawn: farm work, 87-92; name on, 162; show classes, 162-3, 166-7; *see also* Carts; Waggon

Vehicles, motor, *see* Motor lorry; Transporting horses

Vet: buying horse, 29, 31, 78; castration by, 196-7; choice of, 70-1; examining mare, 185; foal, 194; foaling, 190-1, 192; grease, 83; inducing heat, 187, 188, 193; lameness, 80, 82, 83; laminitis, 83; sickness, 74-5, 76; stallion-owner's, 187; testing pregnancy, 188; worming foal, 196; worming horse, 71, 73; wounds, 77

Veterinary certificate: auction sale, 31; insurance, 47

Veterinary fees, insurance of, 47

Visual communication, 68-70

Vulva, 180

Waggon, farm: manoeuvring, 118; shows, 88-9; two-horse, 89, 123; transporting, 45

Wall (horn) of foot, 80, 81, 82, 83

Warble-fly, 73

Warranty, 30-1, 32, 33

Washing, 62-3, **155**

Water in paddocks, 40; stables, 55

Water-bag, 191

Water brush, 63, **58, 155**

Water-cart, *see* Slurry cart

Watering, 50, 55; causing colic, 76

Weaning, 195-6

Weed-killer: poison, 39; distributing, 86

Weeds in paddocks, 39

Weigh-tree, 122-3

Wheat, 53

Wheat straw, 55

Wheels, 88, 92; dangers, 131-2, **132**

Whippens, 123

Whipple-trees, 122-3

White markings on coat, 25-6, **10**

Wind, 76

Window, dangers of, 194; protected, 43

Wind-sucking, 31

'Winking', 180

Wisp, 59

Womb, 179

Wood flour, 63, **155**

Wool for plaiting, 149

Working horses, *see* Farm work; Towns

Workings, 172-4, **10, 171**

Worm paste, 73, 77

Worming, 71, 73; foals, 196; mare away at stud, 186; others' horses, 73

Worms, 39, 71-2, 73; causing colic, 76

Wound dressings, 77

Wounds, 76-7

Yearling, management of, 197-8

Yellow body, 188

Yorkshire halter, 99